College Algebra Practice Workbook

2024

The Most Comprehensive Review of College Algebra

By

Reza Nazari

ISBN: 978-1-63719-549-9

Published by: **Effortless Math Education Inc.**

For Online Math Practice Visit www.EffortlessMath.com

Welcome to
College Algebra Prep

We wholeheartedly appreciate your choice to select Effortless Math as your trusted companion for College Algebra preparation. Taking the College Algebra course is indeed an exceptional step you have taken, a step that deserves high recognition and respect.

This commendable journey you've embarked on underscores the importance of utilizing all available resources to achieve optimal success in your final examination. Our comprehensive practice workbook stands as an invaluable instrument, meticulously designed to propel you to your highest possible score. Trust in its ability to guide you through your studies, refining your understanding and ultimately ensuring your success.

The ***College Algebra Practice Workbook*** is expertly curated to encapsulate the entire spectrum of topics traditionally found within a College Algebra course. This carefully designed workbook offers a myriad of practice problems and quizzes, all aimed at testing and reinforcing your comprehension of the material.

Complementing the workbook are robust online resources that offer a step-by-step guide, a plethora of video tutorials, intuitive lessons, clear examples, and rigorous exercises for each topic. This abundance of resources enables you to validate your solutions, while also enhancing your capacity to independently tackle similar problems.

Crafted with utmost clarity and simplicity, this practice workbook ensures effortless understanding, even for those who have previously faced challenges with mathematics. The inclusion of diverse visual aids such as diagrams, graphs, and charts further facilitates comprehension, providing a more tangible grasp of the abstract concepts.

The ***College Algebra Practice Workbook's*** flexible structure allows it to effortlessly supplement a traditional classroom environment or serve as an autonomous resource for self-study. This meticulously designed workbook equips you with the foundational knowledge necessary to conquer the material and excel in your College Algebra course.

Effortless Math's College Algebra Online Center

Effortless Math Online College Algebra Center offers a complete study program, including the following:

✓ Numerous College Algebra worksheets to help you measure your math skills

✓ Complete Course of College Algebra

✓ Video lessons for all College Algebra topics

✓ Full-length College Algebra practice tests

✓ And much more…

No Registration Required.

Visit EffortlessMath.com/CollegeAlgebra to find your online College Algebra resources.

How to Use This Book Effectively

Look no further when you need a comprehensive practice book to improve your math skills to succeed on the College Algebra course. Each chapter of this workbook to the College Algebra will provide you with the knowledge, tools, and understanding needed for every topic covered on the course.

It is absolutely crucial to thoroughly comprehend each topic before transitioning to the next, as this sequential mastery underpins your academic success. Each topic is accompanied by a QR code which, when scanned, transports you to a dedicated online page.

This page, abundant with instructional resources, offers a trove of enriching videos, practical examples, and a detailed, step-by-step guide to every concept. These invaluable resources aid in deepening your understanding, offering clarity and comprehensive insight into the course material. This interactive learning style ensures not just a basic understanding, but also imparts a solid grasp on the content that you will encounter throughout the course.

To get the best possible results from this book:

➢ **Practice consistently**. Study College Algebra concepts at least 30 to 40 minutes a day. Remember, slow and steady wins the race, which can be applied to preparing for the College Algebra test. Instead of cramming to tackle everything at once, be patient and learn the math topics in short bursts.

➢ Whenever you get a math problem wrong, **mark it off, and review it later** to make sure you understand the concept.

➢ Start each session by **looking over the previous material.**

➢ Once you've reviewed the book's chapters, **take a practice test at the back of the book** to gauge your level of readiness. Then, review your results. Read detailed answers and solutions for each question you missed.

➢ **Take another practice test** to get an idea of how ready you are to take the actual exam. Taking the practice tests will give you the confidence you need on test day. Simulate the College Algebra testing environment by sitting in a quiet room free from distraction. Make sure to clock yourself with a timer.

Looking for more?

Visit EffortlessMath.com/CollegeAlgebra to find hundreds of College Algebra worksheets, video tutorials, practice tests, College Algebra formulas, and much more.

No Registration Required.

Contents

Contents

Contents

Contents

Chapter 1: Fundamentals and Building Blocks

Math Topics that you'll learn in this Chapter:

- ✓ Order of Operations
- ✓ Scientific Notation
- ✓ Exponents Operations
- ✓ Evaluating Expressions
- ✓ Simplifying Algebraic Expressions
- ✓ Sets

1

Chapter 1: Fundamentals and Building Blocks

Order of Operations

✎ *Calculate.*

1) $16 + (30 \div 5) =$

2) $(3 \times 9) \div (-3) =$

3) $57 - (3 \times 8) =$

4) $(-12) \times (7 - 3) =$

5) $(18 - 7) \times (6) =$

6) $(6 \times 10) \div (12 + 3) =$

7) $(13 \times 2) - (24 \div 6) =$

8) $(-5) + (4 \times 3) + 8 =$

9) $(4 \times 2^3) + (16 - 9) =$

10) $(3^2 \times 7) \div (-2 + 1) =$

11) $[-2(48 \div 2^3)] - 6 =$

12) $(-4) + (7 \times 8) + 18 =$

13) $(3 \times 7) + (16 - 7) =$

14) $[3^3 \times (48 \div 2^3)] \div (-2) =$

15) $(14 \times 3) - (3^4 \div 9) =$

16) $(96 \div 12) \times (-3) =$

17) $(48 \div 2^2) \times (-2) =$

18) $(56 \div 7) \times (-5) =$

19) $(-2^2) + (7 \times 9) - 21 =$

20) $(2^4 - 9) \times (-6) =$

21) $[4^3 \times (50 \div 5^2)] \div (-16) =$

22) $(3^2 \times 4^2) \div (-4 + 2) =$

23) $6^2 - (-6 \times 4) + 3 =$

24) $4^2 - (5^2 \times 3) =$

25) $(-4) + (12^2 \div 3^2) - 7^2 =$

26) $(3^2 \times 5) + (-5^2 - 9) =$

27) $2[(3^2 \times 5) \times (-6)] =$

28) $(11^2 - 2^2) - (-7^2) =$

29) $(2^2 \times 5) - (64 \div 8) =$

30) $2[(3^2 \times 4) + (35 \div 5)] =$

31) $(4^2 \times 3) \div (-6) =$

32) $3^2[(4^3 \div 16) - (3^3 \div 27)] =$

Scientific Notation

✎ *Write each number in scientific notation.*

1) $0.114 =$

2) $0.06 =$

3) $8.6 =$

4) $30 =$

5) $60 =$

6) $0.004 =$

7) $78 =$

8) $1,600 =$

9) $1,450 =$

10) $31,000 =$

11) $2,000,000 =$

12) $0.0000003 =$

13) $554,000 =$

14) $0.000725 =$

15) $0.00034 =$

16) $86,000,000 =$

17) $62,000 =$

18) $97,000,000 =$

19) $0.0000045 =$

20) $0.0019 =$

✎ *Write each number in standard notation.*

21) $2 \times 10^{-1} =$

22) $8 \times 10^{-2} =$

23) $1.8 \times 10^{3} =$

24) $9 \times 10^{-4} =$

25) $1.7 \times 10^{-2} =$

26) $9 \times 10^{3} =$

27) $6 \times 10^{4} =$

28) $2.18 \times 10^{5} =$

29) $5 \times 10^{-3} =$

30) $9.4 \times 10^{-5} =$

Exponents Operations

✎ *Simplify and write the answer in exponential form.*

1) $3 \times 3^2 =$

2) $4^3 \times 4 =$

3) $2^2 \times 2^2 =$

4) $6^2 \times 6^2 =$

5) $7^3 \times 7^2 \times 7 =$

6) $2 \times 2^2 \times 2^2 =$

7) $5^3 \times 5^2 \times 5 \times 5 =$

8) $2x \times x =$

9) $x^3 \times x^2 =$

10) $x^4 \times x^4 =$

11) $x^2 \times x^2 \times x^2 =$

12) $6x \times 6x =$

13) $2x^2 \times 2x^2 =$

14) $3x^2 \times x =$

15) $4x^4 \times 4x^4 \times 4x^4 =$

16) $2x^2 \times x^2 =$

17) $x^4 \times 3x =$

18) $x \times 2x^2 =$

19) $5x^4 \times 5x^4 =$

20) $2yx^2 \times 2x =$

21) $3x^4 \times y^2x^4 =$

22) $y^2x^3 \times y^5x^2 =$

23) $4yx^3 \times 2x^2y^3 =$

24) $6x^2 \times 6x^3y^4 =$

25) $3x^4y^5 \times 7x^2y^3 =$

26) $7x^2y^5 \times 9xy^3 =$

27) $7xy^4 \times 4x^3y^3 =$

28) $3x^5y^3 \times 8x^2y^3 =$

29) $6x \times y^5x^2 \times y^3 =$

30) $yx^3 \times 3y^3x^2 \times 2xy =$

31) $5yx^3 \times 4y^2x \times xy^3 =$

32) $6x^2 \times 3x^3y^4 \times 10yx^3 =$

Evaluating Expressions

✎ *Evaluate each expression using the values given.*

1) $3x + 5y$

$x = 3, y = 2$

2) $6x + 5y$

$x = 1, y = 5$

3) $18a + 2b$

$a = 2, b = 8$

4) $4x \div 3y$

$x = 3, y = 2$

5) $-2a + 4b$

$a = 6, b = 3$

6) $4x + 7 - 2y$

$x = 7, y = 6$

7) $5z + 12 - 4k$

$z = 5, k = 2$

8) $2(-x - 2y)$

$x = 6, y = 9$

9) $2x + 15 + 4y$

$x = -2, y = 4$

10) $4a - (15 - b)$

$a = 4, b = 6$

11) $5z + 19 + 8k$

$z = -5, k = 4$

12) $xy + 12 + 5x$

$x = 7, y = 2$

13) $2x + 4y - 3 + 2$

$x = 5, y = 3$

14) $6 + 3(-2x - 3y)$

$x = 9, y = 7$

15) $2x + 14 + 4y$

$x = 6, y = 8$

16) $4a - (5a - b) + 5$

$a = 4, b = 6$

17) $\left(-\frac{12}{x}\right) + 1 + 5y$

$x = 6, y = 8$

18) $(-4)(-2a - 2b)$

$a = 5, b = 3$

19) $10 + 3x + 7 - 2y$

$x = 7, y = 6$

20) $9x + 2 - 4y + 5$

$x = 7, y = 5$

21) $(3a + 6b) - 5b - 9$

$a = -2, b = 3$

22) $-3x - 14 + 7y + 3$

$x = -2, y = -7$

Simplifying Algebraic Expressions

✎ *Simplify each expression.*

1) $3(2x + 1) =$ _____

2) $2(4x - 6) =$ _____

3) $4(3x + 3) =$ _____

4) $2(4x + 5) =$ _____

5) $-3(8x - 7) =$ _____

6) $2x(3x + 4) =$ _____

7) $3x^2 + 3x^2 - 2x^3 =$ _____

8) $2x - x^2 + 6x^3 + 4 =$ _____

9) $5x + 2x^2 - 9x^3 =$ _____

10) $7x^2 + 5x^4 - 2x^3 =$ _____

11) $-3x^2 + 5x^3 + 6x^4 =$ _____

12) $(x - 3)(x - 4) =$ _____

13) $(x - 5)(x + 4) =$ _____

14) $(x - 6)(x - 3) =$ _____

15) $(2x + 5)(x + 8) =$ _____

16) $(3x - 8)(x + 4) =$ _____

17) $-8x^2 + 2x^3 - 10x^4 + 5x =$ _____

18) $11 - 6x^2 + 5x^2 - 12x^3 + 22 =$ _____

19) $3x^2 - 4x + 4x^3 + 10x - 21x =$ _____

20) $10 - 6x^2 + 5x^2 - 3x^3 + 2 =$ _____

21) $3x^5 - 2x^3 + 8x^2 - x^5 =$ _____

22) $(5x^3 - 1) + (4x^3 - 6x^3) =$ _____

Sets

✎ *Write the following sets in the roster form.*

1) The set of all even numbers less than 14.

2) The set of the first 5 odd numbers.

3) The set of all factors of 24.

4) The set of all factors of 36.

5) The set of integers that is between -2 and 3.

6) The set of all prime numbers greater than 1 but less than 30.

7) The set of unique letters in the word "CHOICE".

8) The set of multiples of 4 that are less than 28.

9) The set of prime numbers less than 18.

10) Write the following set in Roster form.

   $A = \{x|x$ is an odd number and is greater than 11 and less than 19$\}$

11) Write the following set in Roster form.

   $A = \{x|x$ is a factor of 45$\}$

12) The set of all $2-$digit numbers whose sum of digits is 8.

Answers – Chapter 1

Order of Operations

1) 22	9) 39	17) -24	25) -37
2) -9	10) -63	18) -40	26) 11
3) 33	11) -18	19) 38	27) -540
4) -48	12) 70	20) -42	28) 166
5) 66	13) 30	21) -8	29) 12
6) 4	14) -81	22) -72	30) 86
7) 22	15) 33	23) 63	31) -8
8) 15	16) -24	24) -59	32) 27

Scientific Notation

1) 1.14×10^{-1}	11) 2×10^6	21) 0.2
2) 6×10^{-2}	12) 3×10^{-7}	22) 0.08
3) 8.6×10^0	13) 5.54×10^5	23) 1,800
4) 3×10^1	14) 7.25×10^{-4}	24) 0.0009
5) 6×10^1	15) 3.4×10^{-4}	25) 0.017
6) 4×10^{-3}	16) 8.6×10^7	26) 9,000
7) 7.8×10^1	17) 6.2×10^4	27) 60,000
8) 1.6×10^3	18) 9.7×10^7	28) 218,000
9) 1.45×10^3	19) 4.5×10^{-6}	29) 0.005
10) 3.1×10^4	20) 1.9×10^{-3}	30) 0.000094

Exponents Operations

1) 3^3

2) 4^4

3) 2^4

4) 6^4

5) 7^6

6) 2^5

7) 5^7

8) $2x^2$

9) x^5

10) x^8

11) x^6

12) $36x^2$

13) $4x^4$

14) $3x^3$

15) $64x^{12}$

16) $2x^4$

17) $3x^5$

18) $2x^3$

19) $25x^8$

20) $4x^3y$

21) $3x^8y^2$

22) x^5y^7

23) $8x^5y^4$

24) $36x^5y^4$

25) $21x^6y^8$

26) $63x^3y^8$

27) $28x^4y^7$

28) $24x^7y^6$

29) $6x^3y^8$

30) $6x^6y^5$

31) $20x^5y^6$

32) $180x^8y^5$

Evaluating Expressions

1) 19

2) 31

3) 52

4) 2

5) 0

6) 23

7) 29

8) −48

9) 27

10) 7

11) 26

12) 61

13) 21

14) −111

15) 58

16) 7

17) 39

18) 64

19) 26

20) 50

21) −12

22) −54

Simplifying Algebraic Expressions

1) $6x + 3$

2) $8x - 12$

3) $12x + 12$

4) $8x + 10$

5) $-24x + 21$

6) $6x^2 + 8x$

7) $-2x^3 + 6x^2$

8) $6x^3 - x^2 + 2x + 4$

9) $-9x^3 + 2x^2 + 5x$

10) $5x^4 - 2x^3 + 7x^2$

11) $6x^4 + 5x^3 - 3x^2$

12) $x^2 - 7x + 12$

13) $x^2 - x - 20$

14) $x^2 - 9x + 18$

15) $2x^2 + 21x + 40$

16) $3x^2 + 4x - 32$

17) $-10x^4 + 2x^3 - 8x^2 + 5x$

18) $-12x^3 - x^2 + 33$

19) $4x^3 + 3x^2 - 15x$

20) $-3x^3 - x^2 + 12$

21) $2x^5 - 2x^3 + 8x^2$

22) $3x^3 - 1$

Sets

1) $\{2, 4, 6, 8, 10, 12\}$

2) $\{1, 3, 5, 7, 9\}$

3) $\{1, 2, 3, 4, 6, 8, 12, 24\}$

4) $\{1, 2, 3, 4, 6, 9, 12, 18, 36\}$

5) $\{-1, 0, 1, 2\}$

6) $\{2, 3, 5, 7, 11, 13, 17, 19, 23, 29\}$

7) $\{C, H, O, I, E\}$

8) $\{4, 8, 12, 16, 20, 24\}$

9) $\{2, 3, 5, 7, 11, 13, 17\}$

10) $A = \{13, 15, 17\}$

11) $A = \{1, 3, 5, 9, 15, 45\}$

12) $\{17, 71, 26, 62, 35, 53, 44, 80\}$

Chapter 2: Equations and Inequalities

Math Topics that you'll learn in this Chapter:

- ✓ Solving Multi–Step Equations
- ✓ Slope and Intercepts
- ✓ Solving Inequalities
- ✓ Graphing Linear Inequalities
- ✓ Solving Compound Inequalities
- ✓ Solving Absolute Value Equations
- ✓ Solving Absolute Value Inequalities
- ✓ Graphing Absolute Value Inequalities
- ✓ Solving Systems of Equations
- ✓ Systems of Equations Word Problems

Solving Multi–Step Equations

✎ *Solve each equation.*

1) $4x - 7 = 13 \Rightarrow x =$ ____

2) $26 = -(x - 4) \Rightarrow x =$ ____

3) $-(5 - x) = 19 \Rightarrow x =$ ____

4) $35 = -x + 14 \Rightarrow x =$ ____

5) $2(3 - 2x) = 10 \Rightarrow x =$ ____

6) $3x - 3 = 15 \Rightarrow x =$ ____

7) $32 = -x + 15 \Rightarrow x =$ ____

8) $-(10 - x) = -13 \Rightarrow x =$ ____

9) $-4(7 + x) = 4 \Rightarrow x =$ ____

10) $22 = 2x - 8 \Rightarrow x =$ ____

11) $-6(3 + x) = 6 \Rightarrow x =$ ____

12) $-3 = 3x - 15 \Rightarrow x =$ ____

13) $-7(12 + x) = 7 \Rightarrow x =$ ____

14) $8(6 - 4x) = 16 \Rightarrow x =$ ____

15) $18 - 4x = -9 - x \Rightarrow x =$ ____

16) $6(4 - x) = 30 \Rightarrow x =$ ____

17) $15 - 3x = -5 - x \Rightarrow x =$ ____

18) $9(-7 - 3x) = 18 \Rightarrow x =$ ____

19) $16 - 2x = -4 - 7x \Rightarrow x =$ ____

20) $14 - 2x = 14 + x \Rightarrow x =$ ____

21) $21 - 3x = -7 - 10x \Rightarrow x =$ ____

22) $8 - 2x = 11 + x \Rightarrow x =$ ____

23) $10 + 12x = -8 + 6x =$ ____

24) $25 + 20x = -5 + 5x =$ ____

25) $16 - x = -8 - 7x \Rightarrow x =$ ____

26) $17 - 3x = 13 + x \Rightarrow x =$ ____

27) $22 + 5x = -8 - x \Rightarrow x =$ ____

28) $-9(7 + x) = 9 \Rightarrow x =$ ____

29) $12 + 2x = -4 - 2x \Rightarrow x =$ ____

30) $12 - x = 2 - 3x \Rightarrow x =$ ____

31) $19 - x = -1 - 11x \Rightarrow x =$ ____

32) $14 - 3x = -5 - 4x \Rightarrow x =$ ____

Slope and Intercepts

✎ *Find the slope of each line.*

1) $y = 2x - 8$, Slope = _____

2) $y = -6x + 3$, Slope = _____

3) $y = -x - 5$, Slope = _____

4) $y = -2x - 9$, Slope = _____

5) $y = 5 + 2x$, Slope = _____

6) $y = 1 - 8x$, Slope = _____

7) $y = -4x + 3$, Slope = _____

8) $y = -9x + 8$, Slope = _____

9) $y = -2x + 4$, Slope = _____

10) $y = 9x - 8$, Slope = _____

11) $y = \frac{1}{2}x + 4$, Slope = _____

12) $y = -\frac{2}{5}x + 7$, Slope = _____

13) $-x + 3y = 5$, Slope = _____

14) $4x + 4y = 6$, Slope = _____

15) $6y - 2x = 10$, Slope = _____

16) $3y - x = 2$, Slope = _____

✎ *Find the slope of the line through each pair of points.*

17) $(4, 4), (8, 12)$, Slope = _____

18) $(-2, 4), (0, 6)$, Slope = _____

19) $(6, -2), (2, 6)$, Slope = _____

20) $(-4, -2), (0, 6)$, Slope = _____

21) $(6, 2), (3, 5)$, Slope = _____

22) $(-5, 1), (-1, 9)$, Slope = _____

23) $(8, 4), (9, 6)$, Slope = _____

24) $(10, -1), (7, 8)$, Slope = _____

25) $(16, -3), (13, -6)$, Slope = _____

26) $(12, 5), (8, 1)$, Slope = _____

27) $(6, 6), (8, 10)$, Slope = _____

28) $(10, -1), (8, 1)$, Slope = _____

Solving Inequalities

✎ *Solve each inequality for x.*

1) $x - 9 < 20 \Rightarrow$ _____

2) $14 \leq -6 + x \Rightarrow$ _____

3) $x - 31 > 9 \Rightarrow$ _____

4) $x + 28 \geq 36 \Rightarrow$ _____

5) $x - 24 > 17 \Rightarrow$ _____

6) $x + 5 \geq 3 \Rightarrow x$_____

7) $x + 14 < 12 \Rightarrow$ _____

8) $26 + x \leq 8 \Rightarrow$ _____

9) $x + 9 \geq -18 \Rightarrow$ _____

10) $x + 24 < 11 \Rightarrow$ _____

11) $17 \leq -5 + x \Rightarrow$ _____

12) $x + 25 > 29 \Rightarrow x$_____

13) $x - 17 \geq 19 \Rightarrow$ _____

14) $x + 8 > -17 \Rightarrow$ _____

15) $x + 8 < -23 \Rightarrow$ _____

16) $16 \leq -5 + x \Rightarrow$ _____

17) $4x \leq 12 \Rightarrow$ _____

18) $28 \geq -7x \Rightarrow$ _____

19) $2x > -14 \Rightarrow$ _____

20) $13x \leq 39 \Rightarrow$ _____

21) $-8x > -16 \Rightarrow$ _____

22) $\frac{x}{2} < -6 \Rightarrow$ _____

23) $\frac{x}{6} > 6 \Rightarrow$ _____

24) $27 \leq \frac{x}{4} \Rightarrow$ _____

25) $\frac{x}{8} < -3 \Rightarrow$ _____

26) $6x \geq 18 \Rightarrow$ _____

27) $5x \geq -25 \Rightarrow$ _____

28) $3x > 45 \Rightarrow$ _____

29) $9x \leq 72 \Rightarrow$ _____

30) $-6x < -36 \Rightarrow$ _____

31) $70 > -10x \Rightarrow$ _____

Graphing Linear Inequalities

✍ *Sketch the group of each linear inequality.*

1) $y < 2x - 1$

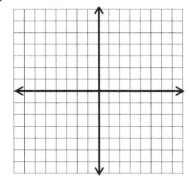

2) $y \geq x - 4$

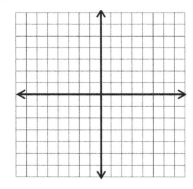

3) $y \geq -4x + 2$

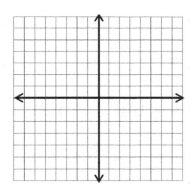

4) $y < -x - 3$

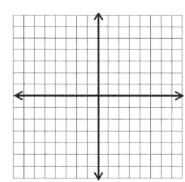

5) $y > -3x + 6$

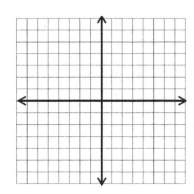

6) $y < 5x - 7$

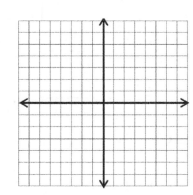

Chapter 2: Equations and Inequalities

Solving Compound Inequalities

✏️ *Solve each inequality.*

1) $2x - 6 \leq 4 \rightarrow$ _____

2) $2 + 3x \geq 17 \rightarrow$ _____

3) $9 + 3x \geq 36 \rightarrow$ _____

4) $2x - 6 \leq 18 \rightarrow$ _____

5) $3x - 4 \leq 23 \rightarrow$ _____

6) $7x - 5 \leq 51 \rightarrow$ _____

7) $4x - 9 \leq 27 \rightarrow$ _____

8) $6x - 11 \leq 13 \rightarrow$ _____

9) $5x - 7 \leq 33 \rightarrow$ _____

10) $6 + 2x \geq 28 \rightarrow$ _____

11) $8 + 3x \geq 35 \rightarrow$ _____

12) $4 + 6x < 34 \rightarrow$ _____

13) $3 + 2x \geq 53 \rightarrow$ _____

14) $7 - 6x > 56 + x \rightarrow$ _____

15) $9 + 4x \geq 39 + 2x \rightarrow$ _____

16) $3 + 5x \geq 43 \rightarrow$ _____

17) $4 - 7x < 60 \rightarrow$ _____

18) $11 - 4x \geq 55 \rightarrow$ _____

19) $12 + x \geq 48 - 2x \rightarrow$ _____

20) $10 - 10x \leq -20 \rightarrow$ _____

21) $5 - 9x \geq -40 \rightarrow$ _____

22) $8 - 7x \geq 36 \rightarrow$ _____

23) $6 + 10x < 69 + 3x \rightarrow$ _____

24) $5 + 4x < 26 - 3x \rightarrow$ _____

25) $10 + 11x < 59 + 4x \rightarrow$ _____

26) $3 + 9x \geq 48 - 6x \rightarrow$ _____

27) $8 - 3x \geq 35 - 6x \rightarrow$ _____

28) $6x - 12 \geq 56 + 4x \rightarrow$ _____

29) $22 - 8x < 67 - 9x \rightarrow$ _____

30) $9x + 11 \geq 67 + 2x \rightarrow$ _____

Solving Absolute Value Equations

✎ *Solve each equation.*

1) $|2x| = 8$

2) $|6x| = 4$

3) $|-3x| = 6$

4) $|9x| = 18$

5) $|-4x| = 24$

6) $|-5x| = 45$

7) $|-7x| = 49$

8) $\left|\dfrac{x}{4}\right| = 9$

9) $\left|\dfrac{x}{6}\right| = 3$

10) $|x + 1| = 4$

11) $\left|\dfrac{x}{6}\right| = 12$

12) $|x - 5| = 12$

13) $|x - 7| = 24$

14) $|x - 10| = 3$

15) $|x| + 2 = 11$

16) $|x| - 4 = 15$

17) $-10|x + 2| = -70$

18) $4|x + 8| = 56$

19) $|x + 12| = 45$

20) $|x - 11| = 22$

21) $|x + 9| = 67$

22) $|3 - x| = 5$

23) $|2 + 3x| = 14$

24) $|-2x - 1| = 11$

25) $|x + 8| - 5 = 2$

26) $6|1 - 5x| - 9 = 57$

Solving Absolute Value Inequalities

✍ *Solve each inequality.*

1) $|2x| > 14$

2) $|4x| < 16$

3) $|x - 2| \leq 6$

4) $|x + 3| > 12$

5) $|x - 9| \geq 32$

6) $|x| - 5 \geq 11$

7) $\left|\frac{x}{6}\right| < 4$

8) $\left|\frac{x-2}{3}\right| > 4$

9) $|x| - 4 < 17$

10) $6 + |x - 8| > 15$

11) $\left|\frac{x}{2} + 3\right| > 6$

12) $\left|\frac{x+5}{4}\right| < 7$

13) $|x| + 4 \geq 6$

14) $|x - 2| - 6 < 5$

15) $3 + |2 + x| < 5$

16) $|x + 7| - 9 < -6$

17) $|x| - 3 > 2$

18) $|x| - 2 > 0$

19) $|3x| \leq 15$

20) $|x + 4| \leq 8$

21) $|3x| \leq 24$

22) $|x - 8| - 10 < -6$

Graphing Absolute Value Inequalities

✎ *Solve each inequality and graph its solution.*

1) $|2x - 2| \geq 10$
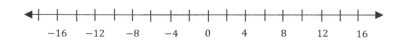

2) $|\frac{1}{3}x - 1| \leq 3$
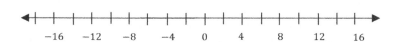

3) $|x| - 2 < 6$

4) $|x + 4| < 8$

5) $|2x - 2| \leq 14$

6) $|x| + 8 > 16$
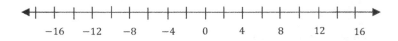

7) $|2x + 8| \leq 24$

8) $|3x - 12| \leq 6$
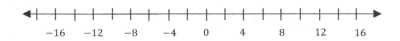

9) $|x| - 6 > 2$

Chapter 2: Equations and Inequalities

Solving Systems of Equations

✍ *Solve each system of equations.*

1) $\begin{cases} x + 2y = 6 \\ 2x - y = 8 \end{cases}$ $x =$ $y =$

8) $\begin{cases} 3y = -6x + 12 \\ 8x - 9y = -10 \end{cases}$ $x =$ $y =$

2) $\begin{cases} 2x + 4y = 6 \\ 4x - 2y = 8 \end{cases}$ $x =$ $y =$

9) $\begin{cases} 3x - 2y = 15 \\ 3x - 5y = 15 \end{cases}$ $x =$ $y =$

3) $\begin{cases} -2x + 2y = -4 \\ 4x - 9y = 28 \end{cases}$ $x =$ $y =$

10) $\begin{cases} -5x + y = -3 \\ 3x - 7y = 21 \end{cases}$ $x =$ $y =$

4) $\begin{cases} x + 8y = -5 \\ 2x + 6y = 0 \end{cases}$ $x =$ $y =$

11) $\begin{cases} x + 15y = 50 \\ x + 10y = 40 \end{cases}$ $x =$ $y =$

5) $\begin{cases} 4x - 3y = -2 \\ x - y = 3 \end{cases}$ $x =$ $y =$

12) $\begin{cases} 3x - 6y = -12 \\ -x - 3y = -6 \end{cases}$ $x =$ $y =$

6) $\begin{cases} 2x + 9y = 17 \\ -3x + 8y = 39 \end{cases}$ $x =$ $y =$

13) $\begin{cases} 3x + 6y = 18 \\ 6x - 3y = 24 \end{cases}$ $x =$ $y =$

7) $\begin{cases} -4x - 6y = 7 \\ 3x - 2y = 7 \end{cases}$ $x =$ $y =$

14) $\begin{cases} 12x - 9y = -6 \\ 3x - 3y = 9 \end{cases}$ $x =$ $y =$

Systems of Equations Word Problems

✍️ *Solve each word problems.*

1) The equations of two lines are $3x - y = 7$ and $2x + 3y = 1$. What is the value of x in the solution for this system of equations? _____

2) The perimeter of a rectangle is 100 feet. The rectangle's length is 10 feet less than 5 times its width. What are the length and width of the rectangle?

   _____

3) A theater sells tickets for a performance. Mr. Smith purchased 8 senior tickets and 5 child tickets for $136 for his friends and family. Mr. Jackson purchased 4 senior tickets and 6 child tickets for $96. What is the price of a senior ticket? $_____

4) The difference between two numbers is 6. Their sum is 14. What is the greater number? $_____

5) The sum of the digits of a certain two–digit number is 7. Reversing its digits increases the number by 9. What is the number? _____

6) The difference between two numbers is 18. Their sum is 66. What are the numbers? _____

Answers – Chapter 2

Solving Multi–Step Equations

1) $x = 5$
2) $x = -22$
3) $x = 24$
4) $x = -21$
5) $x = -1$
6) $x = 6$
7) $x = -17$
8) $x = -3$
9) $x = -8$
10) $x = 15$
11) $x = -4$

12) $x = 4$
13) $x = -13$
14) $x = 1$
15) $x = 9$
16) $x = -1$
17) $x = 10$
18) $x = -3$
19) $x = -4$
20) $x = 0$
21) $x = -4$
22) $x = -1$

23) $x = -3$
24) $x = -2$
25) $x = -4$
26) $x = 1$
27) $x = -5$
28) $x = -8$
29) $x = -4$
30) $x = -5$
31) $x = -2$
32) $x = -19$

Slope and Intercepts

1) 2
2) -6
3) -1
4) -2
5) 2
6) -8
7) -4
8) -9

9) -2
10) 9
11) $\frac{1}{2}$
12) $-\frac{2}{5}$
13) $\frac{1}{3}$
14) -1
15) $\frac{1}{3}$
16) $\frac{1}{3}$
17) 2

18) 1
19) -2
20) 2
21) -1
22) 2
23) 2
24) -3
25) 1
26) 1
27) 2
28) -1

Solving Inequalities

1) $x < 29$

2) $20 \leq x$

3) $x > 40$

4) $x \geq 8$

5) $x > 41$

6) $x \geq -2$

7) $x < -2$

8) $x \leq -18$

9) $x \geq -27$

10) $x < -13$

11) $22 \leq x$

12) $x > 4$

13) $x \geq 36$

14) $x > -25$

15) $x < -31$

16) $21 \leq x$

17) $x \leq 3$

18) $-4 \leq x$

19) $x > -7$

20) $x \leq 3$

21) $x < 2$

22) $x < -12$

23) $x > 36$

24) $108 \leq x$

25) $x < -24$

26) $x \geq 3$

27) $x \geq -5$

28) $x > 15$

29) $x \leq 8$

30) $x > 6$

31) $-7 < x$

Graphing Linear Inequalities

1)

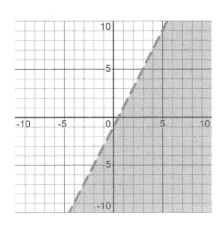

2)

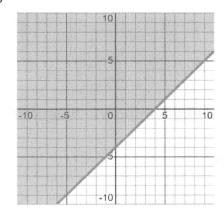

3)

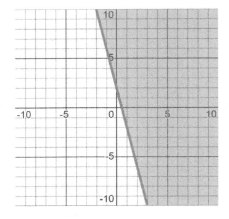

4)

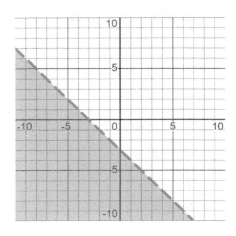

5)

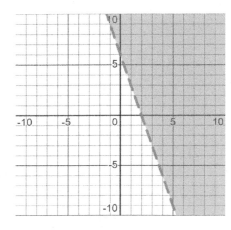

6)

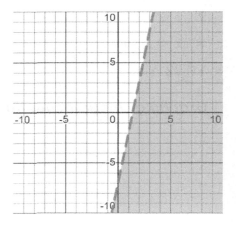

Solving Compound Inequalities

1) $x \leq 5$
2) $x \geq 5$
3) $x \geq 9$
4) $x \leq 12$
5) $x \leq 9$
6) $x \leq 8$
7) $x \leq 9$
8) $x \leq 4$
9) $x \leq 8$
10) $x \geq 11$
11) $x \geq 9$

12) $x < 5$
13) $x \geq 25$
14) $x < -7$
15) $x \geq 15$
16) $x \geq 8$
17) $x > -8$
18) $x \leq -11$
19) $x \geq 12$
20) $x \geq 3$
21) $x \leq 5$
22) $x \leq -4$

23) $x < 9$
24) $x < 3$
25) $x < 7$
26) $x \geq 3$
27) $x \geq 9$
28) $x \geq 34$
29) $x < 45$
30) $x \geq 8$

Solving Absolute Value Equations

1) $x = -4 \ or \ 4$

2) $x = -\frac{2}{3} \ or \ \frac{2}{3}$

3) $x = -2 \ or \ 2$

4) $x = -2 \ or \ 2$

5) $x = -6 \ or \ 6$

6) $x = -9 \ or \ 9$

7) $x = -7 \ or \ 7$

8) $x = -36 \ or \ 36$

9) $x = -18 \ or \ 18$

10) $x = -5 \ or \ 3$

11) $x = -72 \ or \ 72$

12) $x = -7 \ or \ 17$

13) $x = -17 \ or \ 31$

14) $x = 7 \ or \ 13$

15) $x = -9 \ or \ 9$

16) $x = -19 \ or \ 19$

17) $x = -9 \ or \ 5$

18) $x = -22 \ or \ 6$

19) $x = -57 \ or \ 33$

20) $x = -11 \ or \ 33$

21) $x = -76 \ or \ 58$

22) $x = -2 \ or \ 8$

23) $x = -\frac{16}{3} \ or \ 4$

24) $x = -6 \ or \ 5$

25) $x = -15 \ or -1$

26) $x = -2 \ or \ \frac{12}{5}$

Solving Absolute Value Inequalities

1) $x < -7 \ or \ x > 7$

2) $-4 < x < 4$

3) $-4 \le x \le 8$

4) $x < -15 \ or \ x > 9$

5) $x \le -23 \ or \ x \ge 41$

6) $x \le -16 \ or \ x \ge 16$

7) $-24 < x < 24$

8) $x < -10 \ or \ x > 14$

9) $-21 < x < 21$

10) $x > 17 \ or \ x < -1$

11) $x > 6 \ or \ x < -18$

12) $-33 < x < 23$

13) $x \ge 2 \ or \ x \le -2$

14) $x < 13 \ and \ x > -9$

15) $x < 0 \ and \ x > -4$

16) $x < -4 \ and \ x > -10$

17) $x > 5 \ or \ x < -5$

18) $x > 2 \ or \ x < -2$

19) $x \le 5 \ and \ x \ge -5$

20) $-12 \le x \le 4$

21) $x \le 8 \ and \ x \ge -8$

22) $4 < x < 12$

Graphing Absolute Value Inequalities

1) $|2x - 2| \geq 10$

2) $|\frac{1}{3}x - 1| \leq 3$

3) $|x| - 2 < 6$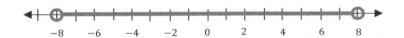

4) $|x + 4| < 8$

5) $|2x - 2| \leq 14$

6) $|x| + 8 > 16$

7) $|2x + 8| \leq 24$

8) $|3x - 12| \leq 6$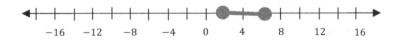

9) $|x| - 6 > 2$

Solving Systems of Equations

1) $x = \frac{22}{5}, y = \frac{4}{5}$

2) $x = \frac{11}{5}, y = \frac{2}{5}$

3) $x = -2, y = -4$

4) $x = 3, y = -1$

5) $x = -11, y = -14$

6) $x = -5, y = 3$

7) $x = \frac{14}{13}, y = -\frac{49}{26}$

8) $x = 1, y = 2$

9) $x = 5, y = 0$

10) $x = 0, y = -3$

11) $x = 20, y = 2$

12) $x = 0, y = 2$

13) $x = \frac{22}{5}, y = \frac{4}{5}$

14) $x = -11, y = -14$

Systems of Equations Word Problems

1) $x = 2$

2) $10, 40$

3) $\$12$

4) 10

5) 34

6) $42, 24$

Chapter 3: Quadratic Function

Math Topics that you'll learn in this Chapter:

- ✓ Solving a Quadratic Equation
- ✓ Graphing Quadratic Functions
- ✓ Solving Quadratic Inequalities
- ✓ Graphing Quadratic Inequalities

Solving a Quadratic Equations

✎ *Solve each equation by factoring or using the quadratic formula.*

1) $(x + 2)(x - 7) = 0$

2) $(x + 3)(x + 5) = 0$

3) $(x - 9)(x + 4) = 0$

4) $(x - 7)(x - 5) = 0$

5) $(x + 4)(x + 8) = 0$

6) $(5x + 7)(x + 4) = 0$

7) $(2x + 5)(4x + 3) = 0$

8) $(3x + 4)(x + 2) = 0$

9) $(6x + 3)(2x + 4) = 0$

10) $(9x + 3)(x + 6) = 0$

11) $x^2 = 2x$

12) $x^2 - 6 = x$

13) $2x^2 + 4 = 6x$

14) $-x^2 - 6 = 5x$

15) $x^2 + 8x = 9$

16) $x^2 + 10x = 24$

17) $x^2 + 7x = -10$

18) $x^2 + 12x = -32$

19) $x^2 + 11x = -28$

20) $x^2 + x - 20 = 2x$

21) $x^2 + 8x = -15$

22) $7x^2 - 14x = -7$

23) $10x^2 = 27x - 18$

24) $7x^2 - 6x + 3 = 3$

25) $2x^2 - 14 = -3x$

26) $10x^2 - 26x = -12$

27) $15x^2 + 80 = -80x$

28) $x^2 + 15x = -56$

29) $6x^2 - 18x - 18 = 6$

30) $2x^2 + 6x - 24 = 12$

31) $2x^2 - 22x + 38 = -10$

32) $-4x^2 - 8x - 3 = -3 - 5x^2$

Graphing Quadratic Functions

✍ *Sketch the graph of each function. Identify the vertex and axis of symmetry.*

1) $y = 3(x + 1)^2 + 2$

2) $y = -(x - 2)^2 - 4$

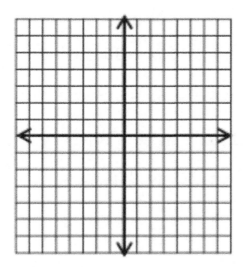 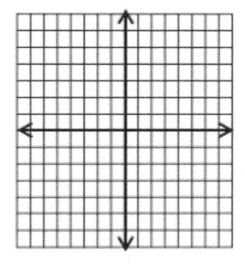

3) $y = 2(x - 3)^2 + 8$

4) $y = x^2 - 8x + 19$

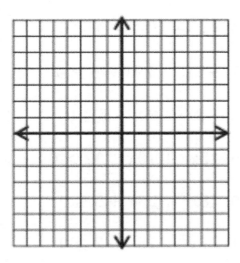 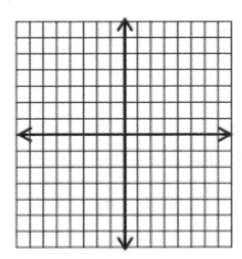

Chapter 3: Quadratic Function

Solving Quadratic Inequalities

✍ *Solve each quadratic inequality.*

1) $x^2 - 1 < 0$

2) $-x^2 - 5x + 6 > 0$

3) $x^2 - 5x - 6 < 0$

4) $x^2 + 4x - 5 > 0$

5) $x^2 - 2x - 3 \geq 0$

6) $x^2 > 5x + 6$

7) $-x^2 - 12x - 11 \leq 0$

8) $x^2 - 2x - 8 \geq 0$

9) $x^2 - 5x - 6 \geq 0$

10) $x^2 + 7x + 10 < 0$

11) $x^2 + 9x + 20 > 0$

12) $x^2 - 8x + 16 > 0$

13) $x^2 - 8x + 12 \leq 0$

14) $x^2 - 11x + 30 \leq 0$

15) $x^2 - 12x + 27 \geq 0$

16) $x^2 - 16x + 64 \geq 0$

17) $x^2 - 36 \leq 0$

18) $x^2 - 13x + 36 \geq 0$

19) $x^2 + 15x + 36 \leq 0$

20) $4x^2 - 6x - 9 > x^2$

21) $5x^2 - 15x + 10 < 0$

22) $3x^2 - 5x \geq 4x^2 + 6$

23) $4x^2 - 12 > 3x^2 + x$

24) $x^2 - 2x \geq x^2 - 6x + 12$

25) $2x^2 + 2x - 8 > x^2$

26) $4x^2 + 20x - 11 < 0$

27) $-9x^2 + 29x - 6 \geq 0$

28) $-8x^2 + 6x - 1 \leq 0$

29) $12x^2 + 10x - 12 > 0$

30) $18x^2 + 23x + 5 \leq 0$

31) $17x^2 + 15x - 2 \geq 0$

32) $3x^2 + 7x \leq 5x^2 + 3x - 6$

Graphing Quadratic Inequalities

✏️ *Sketch the graph of each quadratic inequality.*

1) $y > -2x^2$

2) $y < 3x^2$

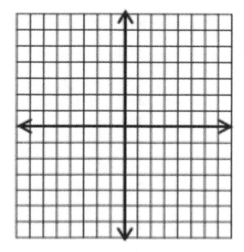
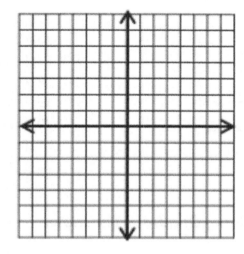

3) $y \geq -3x^2$

4) $y < x^2 + 4$

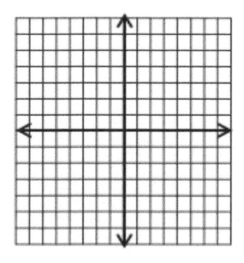
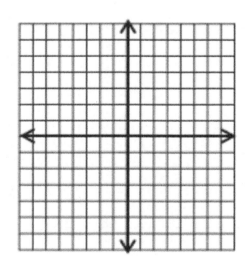

Effortless Math Education

Answers – Chapter 3

Solving a Quadratic Equation

1) $\{-2, 7\}$
2) $\{-3, -5\}$
3) $\{9, -4\}$
4) $\{7, 5\}$
5) $\{-4, -8\}$
6) $\{-\frac{7}{5}, -4\}$
7) $\{-\frac{5}{2}, -\frac{3}{4}\}$
8) $\{-\frac{4}{3}, -2\}$
9) $\{-\frac{1}{2}, -2\}$
10) $\{-\frac{1}{3}, -6\}$

11) $\{2, 0\}$
12) $\{3, -2\}$
13) $\{2, 1\}$
14) $\{-3, -2\}$
15) $\{1, -9\}$
16) $\{2, -12\}$
17) $\{-2, -5\}$
18) $\{-4, -8\}$
19) $\{-4, -7\}$
20) $\{5, -4\}$
21) $\{-5, -3\}$
22) $\{1\}$

23) $\{\frac{6}{5}, \frac{3}{2}\}$
24) $\{\frac{6}{7}, 0\}$
25) $\{-\frac{7}{2}, 2\}$
26) $\{\frac{3}{5}, 2\}$
27) $\{-\frac{4}{3}, -4\}$
28) $\{-8, -7\}$
29) $\{4, -1\}$
30) $\{3, -6\}$
31) $\{3, 8\}$
32) $\{8, 0\}$

Graphing Quadratic Functions

1) $(-1, 2), x = -1$

2) $(2, -4), x = 2$

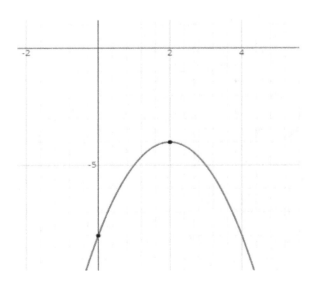

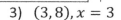
3) $(3, 8), x = 3$

4) $(4, 3), x = 4$

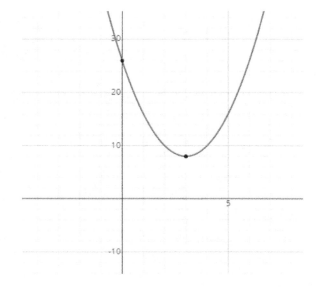

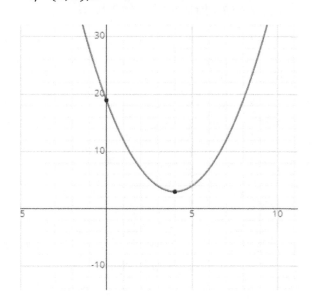

Solving Quadratic Inequalities

1) $-1 < x < 1$
2) $-6 < x < 1$
3) $-1 < x < 6$
4) $x < -5 \text{ or } x > 1$
5) $x \leq -1 \text{ or } x \geq 3$
6) $x < -1 \text{ or } x > 6$
7) $x \leq -11 \text{ or } x \geq -1$
8) $x \leq -2 \text{ or } x \geq 4$
9) $x \leq -1 \text{ or } x \geq 6$
10) $-5 < x < -2$
11) $x < -5 \text{ or } x > -4$
12) $x < 4 \text{ or } x > 4$
13) $2 \leq x \leq 6$
14) $5 \leq x \leq 6$
15) $x \leq 3 \text{ or } x \geq 9$
16) all real numbers
17) $-6 \leq x \leq 6$
18) $x \leq 4 \text{ or } x \geq 9$

19) $-12 \leq x \leq -3$
20) $x < -1 \text{ or } x > 3$
21) $1 < x < 2$
22) $-3 \leq x \leq -2$
23) $x < -3 \text{ or } x > 4$
24) $x \geq 3$
25) $x < -4 \text{ or } x > 2$
26) $-\frac{11}{2} < x < \frac{1}{2}$
27) $\frac{2}{9} \leq x \leq 3$
28) $x \leq \frac{1}{4} \text{ or } x \geq \frac{1}{2}$
29) $x < -1.5 \text{ or } x > \frac{2}{3}$
30) $-1 \leq x \leq -\frac{5}{18}$
31) $x \leq -1 \text{ or } x \geq \frac{2}{17}$
32) $x \leq -1 \text{ or } x \geq 3$

Graphing Quadratic Inequalities

1) $y > -2x^2$

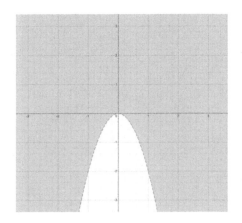

2) $y < 3x^2$

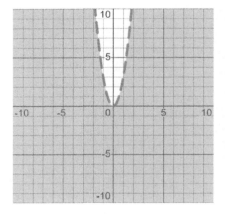

3) $y \geq -3x^2$

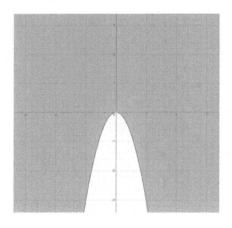

4) $y < x^2 + 4$

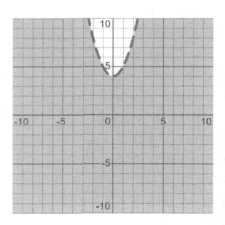

Chapter 4: Complex Numbers

Math Topics that you'll learn in this Chapter:

- ✓ Adding and Subtracting Complex Numbers
- ✓ Multiplying and Dividing Complex Numbers
- ✓ Rationalizing Imaginary Denominators

Chapter 4: Complex Numbers

Adding and Subtracting Complex Numbers

✎ **Simplify.**

1) $(2i) - (i) =$

2) $(2i) + (2i) =$

3) $(i) + (3i) =$

4) $(-2i) - (6i) =$

5) $(5i) + (4i) =$

6) $(3i) - (-7i) =$

7) $(-6i) + (-9i) =$

8) $(15i) - (7i) =$

9) $(-12i) - (5i) =$

10) $(2i) + (2 + 3i) =$

11) $(2 - 4i) + (-i) =$

12) $(-3i) + (3 + 5i) =$

13) $3 + (2 - 4i) =$

14) $(-5i) - (-5 + 2i) =$

15) $(5 + 3i) - (-4i) =$

16) $(8 + 5i) + (-7i) =$

17) $(9i) - (-6i + 10) =$

18) $(12i + 8) + (-7i) =$

19) $(13i) - (17 + 3i) =$

20) $(3 + 5i) + (8 + 3i) =$

21) $(8 - 3i) + (4 + i) =$

22) $(10 + 9i) + (6 + 8i) =$

23) $(-3 + 6i) - (-9 - i) =$

24) $(-5 + 15i) - (-3 + 3i) =$

25) $(-14 + i) - (-12 - 11i) =$

26) $(-18 - 3i) + (11 + 5i) =$

27) $(-11 - 9i) - (-9 - 3i) =$

28) $-8 + (2i) + (-8 + 6i) =$

29) $12 - (5i) + (4 - 14i) =$

30) $-2 + (-8 - 7i) - 9 =$

31) $(-12i) + (2 - 6i) + 10 =$

32) $(-8i) - (8 - 5i) + 6i =$

Multiplying and Dividing Complex Numbers

✎ *Simplify.*

1) $(5i)(-i) =$

2) $(-4i)(5i) =$

3) $(i)(7i)(-i) =$

4) $(3i)(-4i) =$

5) $(-2 - i)(4 + i) =$

6) $(2 - 2i)^2 =$

7) $(4 - 3i)(6 - 6i) =$

8) $(5 + 4i)^2 =$

9) $(4i)(-i)(2 - 5i) =$

10) $(2 - 8i)(3 - 5i) =$

11) $(-5 + 9i)(3 + 5i) =$

12) $(7 + 3i)(7 + 8i) =$

13) $2(3i) - (5i)(-8 + 5i) =$

14) $\frac{5}{-10i} =$

15) $\frac{4 - 3i}{-4i} =$

16) $\frac{5 + 9i}{i} =$

17) $\frac{12i}{-9 + 3i} =$

18) $\frac{-3 - 10i}{5i} =$

19) $\frac{9i}{3 - i} =$

20) $\frac{2 + 4i}{14 + 4i} =$

21) $\frac{5 + 6i}{-1 + 8i} =$

22) $\frac{-8 - i}{-4 - 6i} =$

23) $\frac{-1 + 5i}{-8 - 7i} =$

Chapter 4: Complex Numbers

Rationalizing Imaginary Denominators

✍ *Simplify.*

1) $\dfrac{-2}{-2i} =$

2) $\dfrac{-1}{-9i} =$

3) $\dfrac{-8}{-5i} =$

4) $\dfrac{-5}{-i} =$

5) $\dfrac{3}{5i} =$

6) $\dfrac{6}{-4i} =$

7) $\dfrac{6}{-7i} =$

8) $\dfrac{-10}{3i} =$

9) $\dfrac{a}{bi} =$

10) $\dfrac{10-10i}{-5i} =$

11) $\dfrac{4-9i}{-6i} =$

12) $\dfrac{6+8i}{9i} =$

13) $\dfrac{8i}{-1+3i} =$

14) $\dfrac{5i}{-2-6i} =$

15) $\dfrac{-10-5i}{-6+6i} =$

16) $\dfrac{-5-9i}{9+8i} =$

17) $\dfrac{-5-3i}{7-10i} =$

18) $\dfrac{-1+i}{-5i} =$

19) $\dfrac{-6-i}{i} =$

20) $\dfrac{-4-i}{9+5i} =$

21) $\dfrac{-3+i}{-2i} =$

22) $\dfrac{-6-i}{-1+6i} =$

23) $\dfrac{-9-3i}{-3+3i} =$

24) $\dfrac{4i+1}{-1+3i} =$

Effortless Math Education

Answers – Chapter 4

Adding and Subtracting Complex Numbers

1) i

2) $4i$

3) $4i$

4) $-8i$

5) $9i$

6) $10i$

7) $-15i$

8) $8i$

9) $-17i$

10) $2 + 5i$

11) $2 - 5i$

12) $3 + 2i$

13) $5 - 4i$

14) $5 - 7i$

15) $5 + 7i$

16) $8 - 2i$

17) $-10 + 15i$

18) $8 + 5i$

19) $-17 + 10i$

20) $11 + 8i$

21) $12 - 2i$

22) $16 + 17i$

23) $6 + 7i$

24) $-2 + 12i$

25) $-2 + 12i$

26) $-7 + 2i$

27) $-2 - 6i$

28) $-16 + 8i$

29) $16 - 19i$

30) $-19 - 7i$

31) $12 - 18i$

32) $-8 + 3i$

Multiplying and Dividing Complex Numbers

1) 5

2) 20

3) $7i$

4) 12

5) $-7 - 6i$

6) $-8i$

7) $6 - 42i$

8) $9 + 40i$

9) $8 - 20i$

10) $-34 - 34i$

11) $-60 + 2i$

12) $25 + 77i$

13) $25 + 46i$

14) $\frac{i}{2}$

15) $\frac{3}{4} + i$

16) $9 - 5i$

17) $\frac{2}{5} - \frac{6}{5}i$

18) $-2 + \frac{3}{5}i$

19) $-\frac{9}{10} + \frac{27}{10}i$

20) $\frac{11}{53} + \frac{12}{53}i$

21) $\frac{43}{65} - \frac{46}{65}i$

22) $\frac{19}{26} - \frac{11}{13}i$

23) $-\frac{27}{113} - \frac{47}{113}i$

Rationalizing Imaginary Denominators

1) $-i$

2) $-\frac{1}{9}i$

3) $\frac{-8}{5}i$

4) $-5i$

5) $-\frac{3}{5}i$

6) $\frac{3}{2}i$

7) $\frac{6}{7}i$

8) $\frac{10}{3}i$

9) $-\frac{a}{b}i$

10) $2 + 2i$

11) $\frac{3}{2} + \frac{2}{3}i$

12) $\frac{8}{9} - \frac{2}{3}i$

13) $\frac{12}{5} - \frac{4}{5}i$

14) $-\frac{3}{4} - \frac{1}{4}i$

15) $\frac{5}{12} + \frac{5}{4}i$

16) $-\frac{117}{145} - \frac{41}{145}i$

17) $-\frac{5}{149} - \frac{71}{149}i$

18) $-\frac{1}{5} - \frac{1}{5}i$

19) $-1 + 6i$

20) $-\frac{41}{106} + \frac{11}{106}i$

21) $-\frac{1}{2} - \frac{3}{2}i$

22) i

23) $1 + 2i$

24) $\frac{11}{10} - \frac{7}{10}i$

Chapter 5: Matrices

Math Topics that you'll learn in this Chapter:

- ✓ Adding and Subtracting Matrices
- ✓ Matrix Multiplications
- ✓ Finding Determinants of a Matrix

43

Chapter 5: Matrices

Adding and Subtracting Matrices

✎ *Solve.*

1) $[2 \quad -5 \quad -3] + [1 \quad -2 \quad -3] =$

2) $\begin{bmatrix} 3 & -6 \\ -1 & -3 \\ -5 & -1 \end{bmatrix} + \begin{bmatrix} 0 & -1 \\ 6 & 3 \\ 2 & 3 \end{bmatrix} =$

3) $\begin{bmatrix} -5 & 2 & -2 \\ 4 & -2 & 0 \end{bmatrix} - \begin{bmatrix} 6 & -5 & -6 \\ 1 & 3 & -3 \end{bmatrix} =$

4) $\begin{bmatrix} 2 & 1 \\ -1 & 3 \end{bmatrix} - \begin{bmatrix} 2 & 5 \\ -7 & -2 \end{bmatrix} =$

5) $\begin{bmatrix} 6 & 4 \\ -9 & 7 \end{bmatrix} + \begin{bmatrix} 5 & 3 \\ -4 & 1 \end{bmatrix} =$

6) $\begin{bmatrix} 2 & 0 \\ -1 & 1 \end{bmatrix} - \begin{bmatrix} 4 & -2 \\ 2 & 1 \end{bmatrix} =$

7) $\begin{bmatrix} 6 & -7 \\ -3 & 11 \end{bmatrix} + \begin{bmatrix} 10 & -11 \\ 12 & 18 \end{bmatrix} =$

8) $\begin{bmatrix} -1 & 2 & -1 \\ 2 & -1 & 0 \end{bmatrix} - \begin{bmatrix} 2 & -5 & -4 \\ 1 & 1 & -3 \end{bmatrix} =$

9) $\begin{bmatrix} 8 & 12 \\ 14 & 21 \end{bmatrix} + \begin{bmatrix} 8 & -15 \\ 10 & -7 \end{bmatrix} =$

10) $\begin{bmatrix} 12 \\ 9 \\ 5 \end{bmatrix} + \begin{bmatrix} 18 \\ -14 \\ 19 \end{bmatrix} =$

11) $\begin{bmatrix} 14 \\ -16 \\ 13 \\ 21 \end{bmatrix} + \begin{bmatrix} -16 \\ 8 \\ -5 \\ -18 \end{bmatrix} =$

12) $\begin{bmatrix} 2 & -5 & -9 \\ 4 & -7 & 11 \\ -6 & 3 & -17 \end{bmatrix} + \begin{bmatrix} 3 & 4 & -5 \\ 13 & 2 & 5 \\ 4 & -8 & 1 \end{bmatrix} =$

13) $\begin{bmatrix} 1 & -7 & 5 \\ 31 & 3 & 18 \\ 22 & 6 & 4 \end{bmatrix} + \begin{bmatrix} 13 & 17 & 5 \\ 3 & 8 & -1 \\ -9 & 2 & 12 \end{bmatrix} =$

14) $\begin{bmatrix} 2 & 4 & 6 \\ 1 & 3 & 5 \end{bmatrix} - \begin{bmatrix} 1 & 2 & -1 \\ 3 & -1 & 4 \end{bmatrix} =$

15) $\begin{bmatrix} 2 & 1 \\ -1 & 3 \\ 6 & -2 \end{bmatrix} + \begin{bmatrix} -1 & 5 \\ 7 & -2 \\ 3 & 5 \end{bmatrix} =$

16) $\begin{bmatrix} -1 & -2 \\ 4 & 6 \\ 3 & -1 \end{bmatrix} + \begin{bmatrix} 4 & 6 \\ 8 & 1 \\ 1 & -3 \end{bmatrix} =$

Matrix Multiplications

✏️ *Solve.*

1) $\begin{bmatrix} 5 \\ 6 \\ 0 \end{bmatrix} \begin{bmatrix} 3 & -1 \end{bmatrix} =$

2) $\begin{bmatrix} -5 & -5 \\ -1 & 2 \end{bmatrix} \begin{bmatrix} -2 & -3 \\ 3 & 5 \end{bmatrix} =$

3) $\begin{bmatrix} 0 & 5 \\ -3 & 1 \\ -5 & 1 \end{bmatrix} \begin{bmatrix} -4 & 4 \\ -2 & -4 \end{bmatrix} =$

4) $\begin{bmatrix} 5 & 3 & 5 \\ 1 & 5 & 0 \end{bmatrix} \begin{bmatrix} -4 & 2 \\ -3 & 4 \\ 3 & -5 \end{bmatrix} =$

5) $\begin{bmatrix} 3 & -1 \\ -3 & 6 \\ -6 & -6 \end{bmatrix} \begin{bmatrix} -1 & 6 \\ 5 & 4 \end{bmatrix} =$

6) $\begin{bmatrix} -2 & -6 \\ -4 & 3 \\ 5 & 0 \\ 4 & -6 \end{bmatrix} \begin{bmatrix} 2 & -2 & 2 \\ -2 & 0 & -3 \end{bmatrix} =$

7) $\begin{bmatrix} -1 & 0 & 3 \end{bmatrix} \begin{bmatrix} 1 \\ 2 \\ -1 \end{bmatrix} =$

8) $\begin{bmatrix} -1 \\ 6 \\ -6 \end{bmatrix} \begin{bmatrix} 8 & 5 & 4 \end{bmatrix} =$

9) $\begin{bmatrix} 0 & 2 \\ 2 & -1 \end{bmatrix} \begin{bmatrix} -2 & 1 \\ 1 & 4 \end{bmatrix} =$

10) $\begin{bmatrix} 2 & 4 & 3 \\ 4 & 3 & 2 \end{bmatrix} \begin{bmatrix} 4 & 3 \\ 5 & 5 \\ 2 & 5 \end{bmatrix} =$

11) $\begin{bmatrix} 2 & 5 \\ -4 & -3 \end{bmatrix} \begin{bmatrix} 1 & -5 \\ 3 & 2 \end{bmatrix} =$

12) $\begin{bmatrix} 1 & -2 \\ -4 & 5 \end{bmatrix} \begin{bmatrix} 4 & 3 \\ 4 & 0 \end{bmatrix} =$

13) $\begin{bmatrix} 3 & 1 & 2 \\ -5 & 6 & 5 \end{bmatrix} \begin{bmatrix} 3 \\ 5 \\ 2 \end{bmatrix} =$

14) $\begin{bmatrix} -1 & 2 & 5 \\ 0 & -2 & -1 \end{bmatrix} \begin{bmatrix} 5 & 1 \\ 2 & -2 \\ 0 & 1 \end{bmatrix} =$

15) $\begin{bmatrix} 2 & 3 \\ 5 & 7 \\ -2 & -1 \end{bmatrix} \begin{bmatrix} 2 & 4 \\ 5 & 3 \end{bmatrix} =$

16) $\begin{bmatrix} -3 & 5 \\ 9 & 1 \\ 3 & 2 \end{bmatrix} \begin{bmatrix} -2 & 1 & 5 \\ 8 & 2 & -6 \end{bmatrix} =$

Finding Determinants of a Matrix

✍ *Evaluate the determinant of each matrix.*

1) $\begin{bmatrix} 2 & 5 \\ 3 & 8 \end{bmatrix} =$

2) $\begin{bmatrix} 8 & -6 \\ -10 & 9 \end{bmatrix} =$

3) $\begin{bmatrix} 2 & -2 \\ 7 & -7 \end{bmatrix} =$

4) $\begin{bmatrix} -5 & 0 \\ 3 & 10 \end{bmatrix} =$

5) $\begin{bmatrix} 0 & 6 \\ -6 & 0 \end{bmatrix} =$

6) $\begin{bmatrix} 3 & 4 \\ 2 & -6 \end{bmatrix} =$

7) $\begin{bmatrix} 8 & 5 \\ -4 & -6 \end{bmatrix} =$

8) $\begin{bmatrix} 0 & 4 \\ 6 & 5 \end{bmatrix} =$

9) $\begin{bmatrix} 6 & 1 & 7 \\ 2 & -3 & 3 \\ 4 & -1 & 2 \end{bmatrix} =$

10) $\begin{bmatrix} -2 & 5 & -4 \\ 0 & -3 & 5 \\ -5 & 5 & -6 \end{bmatrix} = 0$

11) $\begin{bmatrix} -3 & 1 & 8 \\ -9 & -1 & 7 \\ 0 & 2 & 1 \end{bmatrix} =$

12) $\begin{bmatrix} 5 & 3 & 3 \\ -4 & -5 & 1 \\ 5 & 3 & 0 \end{bmatrix} =$

13) $\begin{bmatrix} 6 & 2 & -1 \\ -5 & -4 & -5 \\ 3 & -3 & 1 \end{bmatrix} =$

14) $\begin{bmatrix} 6 & 5 & -3 \\ -5 & 4 & -2 \\ 1 & -4 & 5 \end{bmatrix} =$

15) $\begin{bmatrix} -2 & -1 & 3 \\ 5 & 11 & -2 \\ -1 & 5 & 1 \end{bmatrix} =$

16) $\begin{bmatrix} 3 & 9 & 1 \\ 2 & -10 & 1 \\ 5 & 3 & 8 \end{bmatrix} =$

17) $\begin{bmatrix} 6 & 4 & 2 \\ 3 & -7 & 1 \\ 5 & 5 & 3 \end{bmatrix} =$

18) $\begin{bmatrix} -1 & -8 & 9 \\ 4 & 12 & -7 \\ -10 & 3 & 2 \end{bmatrix} =$

19) $\begin{bmatrix} 5 & 4 & 7 \\ 3 & -6 & 5 \\ 4 & 2 & -3 \end{bmatrix} =$

20) $\begin{bmatrix} 3 & 4 & 1 \\ 2 & 5 & -2 \\ -1 & 6 & -3 \end{bmatrix} =$

Answers – Chapter 5

Adding and Subtracting Matrices

1) $\begin{bmatrix} 3 & -7 & -6 \end{bmatrix}$

2) $\begin{bmatrix} 3 & -7 \\ 5 & 0 \\ -3 & 2 \end{bmatrix}$

3) $\begin{bmatrix} -11 & 7 & 4 \\ 3 & -5 & 3 \end{bmatrix}$

4) $\begin{bmatrix} 0 & -4 \\ 6 & 5 \end{bmatrix}$

5) $\begin{bmatrix} 11 & 7 \\ -13 & 8 \end{bmatrix}$

6) $\begin{bmatrix} -2 & 2 \\ -3 & 0 \end{bmatrix}$

7) $\begin{bmatrix} 16 & -18 \\ 9 & 29 \end{bmatrix}$

8) $\begin{bmatrix} -3 & 7 & 3 \\ 1 & -2 & 3 \end{bmatrix}$

9) $\begin{bmatrix} 16 & -3 \\ 24 & 14 \end{bmatrix}$

10) $\begin{bmatrix} 30 \\ -5 \\ 24 \end{bmatrix}$

11) $\begin{bmatrix} -2 \\ -8 \\ 8 \\ 3 \end{bmatrix}$

12) $\begin{bmatrix} 5 & -1 & -14 \\ 17 & -5 & 16 \\ -2 & -5 & -16 \end{bmatrix}$

13) $\begin{bmatrix} 14 & 10 & 10 \\ 34 & 11 & 17 \\ 13 & 8 & 16 \end{bmatrix}$

14) $\begin{bmatrix} 1 & 2 & 7 \\ -2 & 4 & 1 \end{bmatrix}$

15) $\begin{bmatrix} 1 & 6 \\ 6 & 1 \\ 9 & 3 \end{bmatrix}$

16) $\begin{bmatrix} 3 & 4 \\ 12 & 7 \\ 4 & -4 \end{bmatrix}$

Matrix Multiplications

1) $\begin{bmatrix} 15 & -5 \\ 18 & -6 \\ 0 & 0 \end{bmatrix}$

2) $\begin{bmatrix} -5 & -10 \\ 8 & 13 \end{bmatrix}$

3) $\begin{bmatrix} -10 & -20 \\ 10 & -16 \\ 18 & -24 \end{bmatrix}$

4) $\begin{bmatrix} -14 & -3 \\ -19 & 22 \end{bmatrix}$

5) $\begin{bmatrix} -8 & 14 \\ 33 & 6 \\ -24 & -60 \end{bmatrix}$

6) $\begin{bmatrix} 8 & 4 & 14 \\ -14 & 8 & -17 \\ 10 & -10 & 10 \\ 20 & -8 & 26 \end{bmatrix}$

7) $\begin{bmatrix} -4 \end{bmatrix}$

8) $\begin{bmatrix} -8 & -5 & -4 \\ 48 & 30 & 24 \\ -48 & -30 & -24 \end{bmatrix}$

9) $\begin{bmatrix} 2 & 8 \\ -5 & -2 \end{bmatrix}$

10) $\begin{bmatrix} 34 & 41 \\ 35 & 37 \end{bmatrix}$

11) $\begin{bmatrix} 17 & 0 \\ -13 & 14 \end{bmatrix}$

12) $\begin{bmatrix} -4 & 3 \\ 4 & -12 \end{bmatrix}$

13) $\begin{bmatrix} 18 \\ 25 \end{bmatrix}$

14) $\begin{bmatrix} -1 & 0 \\ -4 & 3 \end{bmatrix}$

15) $\begin{bmatrix} 19 & 17 \\ 45 & 41 \\ -9 & -11 \end{bmatrix}$

16) $\begin{bmatrix} 46 & 7 & -45 \\ -10 & 11 & 39 \\ 10 & 7 & 3 \end{bmatrix}$

Finding Determinants of a Matrix

1) 1	8) -24	15) 69
2) 12	9) 60	16) -292
3) 0	10) -51	17) -72
4) -50	11) -90	18) 647
5) 36	12) 39	19) 366
6) -26	13) -161	20) 40
7) -28	14) 139	

Chapter 6: Polynomial Operations

Math Topics that you'll learn in this Chapter:

- ✓ Writing Polynomials in Standard Form
- ✓ Simplifying Polynomials
- ✓ Adding and Subtracting Polynomials
- ✓ Multiplying and Dividing Monomials
- ✓ Multiplying a Polynomial and a Monomial
- ✓ Multiplying Binomials
- ✓ Factoring Trinomials
- ✓ Operations with Polynomials
- ✓ End Behavior of Polynomial Functions
- ✓ Polynomial Division (Long Division)
- ✓ Polynomial Division (Synthetic Division)
- ✓ Finding Zeros of Polynomials
- ✓ Polynomial Identities

Chapter 6: Polynomial Operations

Writing Polynomials in Standard Form

✎ *Write polynomials in standard form.*

1) $10x - 7x =$

2) $-3 + 12x - 12x =$

3) $3x^2 - 4x^3 =$

4) $6 + 4x^3 - 6 =$

5) $2x^2 + 1x - 7x^3 =$

6) $-x^2 + 4x^3 =$

7) $2x + 4x^3 - 2x^2 =$

8) $-2x^2 + 4x - 6x^3 =$

9) $2x^2 + 2 - 5x =$

10) $12 - 7x + 9x^4 =$

11) $5x^2 + 13x - 2x^3 =$

12) $10 + 6x^2 - x^3 =$

13) $12x^2 - 7x + 9x^3 =$

14) $5x^4 - 3x^2 - 2x^3 =$

15) $-12 + 3x^2 - 6x^4 =$

16) $5x^2 - 9x^5 + 8x^3 - 11 =$

17) $4x^2 - 2x^5 + 14 - 7x^4 =$

18) $-x^2 + 2x - 5x^3 - 4x =$

19) $8x^5 + 11x^3 - 6x^5 - 8x^2 =$

20) $5x^2 - 12x^4 + 4x^2 + 5x^3 =$

21) $7x^3 - 6x^4 - 3x^2 + 22x^3 =$

22) $9x^2 + x^4 + 12x^3 - 5x^4 =$

23) $3x(2x + 5 - 2x^2) =$

24) $11x(x^5 + 2x^3) =$

25) $5x(3x^2 + 2x + 1) =$

26) $7x(3 - x + 6x^3) =$

27) $2x(3x^2 - 4x^4 + 3) =$

28) $6x(4x^5 + 7x^3 - 2) =$

29) $-4x(5x^2 - 6x + 3x^3) =$

30) $9x(-2x^3 + 3 - 6x) =$

31) $2x^2(3x - 16 + 2x^2) =$

32) $-3x^2(-2x^3 + 2x^2 + 28) =$

Simplifying Polynomials

✎ *Simplify each expression.*

1) $4(2x - 10) =$

2) $2x(3x - 2) =$

3) $3x(5x - 3) =$

4) $2x(7x + 3) =$

5) $4x(8x - 4) =$

6) $5x(6x + 4) =$

7) $(2x - 3)(x - 4) =$

8) $(x - 5)(3x + 4) =$

9) $(x - 5)(x - 3) =$

10) $(3x + 8)(3x - 8) =$

11) $(3x - 8)(3x - 4) =$

12) $3x^2 + 3x^2 - 2x^3 =$

13) $2x - x^2 + 6x^3 + 4 =$

14) $5x + 2x^2 - 9x^3 =$

15) $8x^2 - 3x^3 - 9x =$

16) $5x^3 + 2x^4 - 7x^2 =$

17) $-4x^5 - 6x^2 + 2x^4 =$

18) $2x^4 + 3x^2 - 3x^3 - 2x =$

19) $7x^2 + 5x^4 - 2x^3 =$

20) $-3x^2 + 5x^3 + 6x^4 =$

21) $-8x^2 + 2x^3 - 10x^4 + 5x =$

22) $11 - 6x^2 + 5x^2 - 12x^3 + 22 =$

23) $2x^2 - 2x + 3x^3 + 12x - 22x =$

24) $11 - 4x^2 + 3x^2 - 7x^3 + 3 =$

25) $2x^5 - x^3 + 8x^2 - 2x^5 =$

26) $(2x^3 - 1) + (3x^3 - 2x^3) =$

27) $3(4x^4 - 4x^3 - 5x^4) =$

28) $-5(x^6 + 10) - 8(14 - x^6) =$

29) $3x^2 - 5x^3 - x + 10 - 2x^2 =$

30) $11 - 3x^2 + 2x^2 - 5x^3 + 7 =$

31) $(8x^2 - 3x) - (5x - 5 - 8x^2) =$

32) $3x^2 - 5x^3 - x(2x^2 + 4x) =$

Chapter 6: Polynomial Operations

Adding and Subtracting Polynomials

✎ *Add or subtract expressions.*

1) $(x^2 - 5) + (x^2 + 6) =$ _____

2) $(2x^2 - 6) - (3 - 2x^2) =$ _____

3) $(x^3 + 3x^2) - (x^3 + 6) =$ _____

4) $(4x^3 - x^2) + (6x^2 - 8x) =$ _____

5) $(2x^3 + 3x) - (5x^3 + 2) =$ _____

6) $(5x^3 - 2) + (2x^3 + 10) =$ _____

7) $(7x^3 + 5) - (9 - 4x^3) =$ _____

8) $(5x^2 + 3x^3) - (2x^3 + 6) =$ _____

9) $(8x^2 - x) + (4x - 8x^2) =$ _____

10) $(6x + 9x^2) - (5x + 2) =$ _____

11) $(7x^4 - 2x) - (6x - 2x^4) =$ _____

12) $(2x - 4x^3) - (9x^3 + 6x) =$ _____

13) $(8x^3 - 8x^2) - (6x^2 - 3x) =$ _____

14) $(9x^2 - 6) + (5x^2 - 4x^3) =$ _____

15) $(8x^3 + 3x^4) - (x^4 - 3x^3) =$ _____

16) $(-4x^3 - 2x) + (5x - 2x^3) =$ _____

17) $(9x - 5x^4) - (8x^4 + 4x) =$ _____

18) $(8x - 3x^2) - (7x^4 - 3x^2) =$ _____

19) $(9x^3 - 7) + (5x^3 - 4x^2) =$ _____

20) $(7x^3 + x^4) - (6x^4 - 5x^3) =$ _____

Multiplying and Dividing Monomials

✍ *Simplify each expression.*

1) $(3x^5)(2x^2) =$

_____

2) $(6x^5)(2x^4) =$

_____

3) $(-7x^9)(2x^5) =$

_____

4) $(7x^7y^9)(-5x^6y^6) =$

_____

5) $(8x^5y^6)(3x^2y^5) =$

_____

6) $(8yx^2)(7y^5x^3) =$

_____

7) $(4x^2y)(2x^2y^3) =$

_____

8) $(-2x^9y^4)(-9x^6y^8) =$

_____

9) $(-5x^8y^2)(-6x^4y^5) =$

_____

10) $(8x^8y)(-7x^4y^3) =$

_____

11) $(9x^6y^2)(6x^7y^4) =$

_____

12) $(8x^9y^5)(6x^5y^4) =$

_____

13) $(-5x^8y^9)(7x^7y^8) =$

_____

14) $(6x^2y^5)(5x^3y^2) =$

_____

15) $(9x^5y^{12})(4x^7y^9) =$

_____

16) $(-10x^{14}y^8)(2x^7y^5) =$

_____

17) $\frac{6x^5y^7}{xy^6} =$

_____

18) $\frac{9x^6y^6}{3x^4y} =$

_____

19) $\frac{16x^4y^6}{4xy} =$

_____

Chapter 6: Polynomial Operations

Multiplying a Polynomial and a Monomial

✍ *Find each product.*

1) $x(x - 5) =$

_____

2) $2(3 + x) =$

_____

3) $x(x - 7) =$

_____

4) $x(x + 9) =$

_____

5) $2x(x - 2) =$

_____

6) $5(4x + 3) =$

_____

7) $4x(3x - 4) =$

_____

8) $x(5x + 2y) =$

_____

9) $3x(x - 2y) =$

_____

10) $6x(3x - 4y) =$

_____

11) $2x(3x - 8) =$

_____

12) $6x(4x - 6y) =$

_____

13) $3x(4x - 2y) =$

_____

14) $2x(2x - 6y) =$

_____

15) $5x(x^2 + y^2) =$

_____

16) $3x(2x^2 - y^2) =$

_____

17) $6(9x^2 + 3y^2) =$

_____

18) $4x(-3x^2y + 2y) =$

_____

19) $-3(6x^2 - 5xy + 3) =$

_____

20) $6(x^2 - 4xy - 3) =$

_____

Multiplying Binomials

✎ *Find each product.*

1) $(x-3)(x+4) =$

_____

2) $(x+3)(x+5) =$

_____

3) $(x-6)(x-7) =$

_____

4) $(x-9)(x-4) =$

_____

5) $(x-7)(x-5) =$

_____

6) $(x+6)(x+2) =$

_____

7) $(x-9)(x+3) =$

_____

8) $(x-8)(x-5) =$

_____

9) $(x+3)(x+7) =$

_____

10) $(x-9)(x+4) =$

_____

11) $(x+6)(x+6) =$

_____

12) $(x+7)(x+7) =$

_____

13) $(x-8)(x+7) =$

_____

14) $(x+9)(x+9) =$

_____

15) $(x-8)(x-8) =$

_____

16) $(x-9)(x+5) =$

_____

17) $(2x-5)(x+4) =$

_____

18) $(2x+6)(x+3) =$

_____

19) $(2x+4)(x+5) =$

_____

20) $(2x-3)(2x+2) =$

_____

Factoring Trinomials

✎ *Factor each trinomial.*

1) $x^2 + 5x + 4 =$

_____

2) $x^2 + 5x + 6 =$

_____

3) $x^2 - 4x + 3 =$

_____

4) $x^2 - 10x + 25 =$

_____

5) $x^2 - 13x + 40 =$

_____

6) $x^2 + 8x + 12 =$

_____

7) $x^2 - 6x - 27 =$

_____

8) $x^2 - 14x + 48 =$

_____

9) $x^2 + 15x + 56 =$

_____

10) $x^2 - 5x - 36 =$

_____

11) $x^2 + 12x + 36 =$

_____

12) $x^2 + 16x + 63 =$

_____

13) $x^2 + x - 72 =$

_____

14) $x^2 + 18x + 81 =$

_____

15) $x^2 - 16x + 64 =$

_____

16) $x^2 - 18x + 81 =$

_____

17) $2x^2 + 10x + 8 =$

_____

18) $2x^2 + 4x - 6 =$

_____

19) $2x^2 + 9x + 4 =$

_____

20) $4x^2 + 4x - 24 =$

_____

Chapter 6: Polynomial Operations

Operations with Polynomials

✍ *Find each product.*

1) $2(3x + 2) =$

2) $-3(2x + 5) =$

3) $4(7x - 3) =$

4) $5(2x - 4) =$

5) $3x(2x - 7) =$

6) $-2x(3x + 4) =$

7) $4x(4x - 6) =$

8) $x^2(3x + 4) =$

9) $x^3(x + 5) =$

10) $x^4(5x - 3) =$

11) $9(6x + 2) =$

12) $8(3x + 7) =$

13) $5(6x - 1) =$

14) $-3(8x - 3) =$

15) $3x^2(6x - 5) =$

16) $5x^2(7x - 2) =$

17) $6x^3(-3x + 4) =$

18) $-7x^4(2x - 4) =$

19) $8(x^2 + 2x - 3) =$

20) $4(4x^2 - 2x + 1) =$

21) $2(3x^2 + 2x - 2) =$

22) $8x(5x^2 + 3x + 8) =$

23) $(9x + 1)(3x - 1) =$

24) $(4x + 5)(6x - 5) =$

25) $(7x + 3)(5x - 6) =$

26) $(3x - 4)(3x + 8) =$

End Behavior of Polynomial Functions

✎ *Find the end behavior of the functions.*

1) $f(x) = x^2 - 3x + 5$

$f(x) \rightarrow$ ___, as $x \rightarrow$ ___
$f(x) \rightarrow$ ___, as $x \rightarrow$ ___

2) $f(x) = -x^2 - 3x$

$f(x) \rightarrow$ ___, as $x \rightarrow$ ___
$f(x) \rightarrow$ ___, as $x \rightarrow$ ___

3) $f(x) = x^3 - 4x + 2$

$f(x) \rightarrow$ ___, as $x \rightarrow$ ___
$f(x) \rightarrow$ ___, as $x \rightarrow$ ___

4) $f(x) = -x^3 + 3x^2$

$f(x) \rightarrow$ ___, as $x \rightarrow$ ___
$f(x) \rightarrow$ ___, as $x \rightarrow$ ___

5) $f(x) = x^2 - 6x + 12$

$f(x) \rightarrow$ ___, as $x \rightarrow$ ___
$f(x) \rightarrow$ ___, as $x \rightarrow$ ___

6) $f(x) = x^3 + 8x + 16$

$f(x) \rightarrow$ ___, as $x \rightarrow$ ___
$f(x) \rightarrow$ ___, as $x \rightarrow$ ___

7) $f(x) = x^5 - 4x^3 + 4x + 2$

$f(x) \rightarrow$ ___, as $x \rightarrow$ ___
$f(x) \rightarrow$ ___, as $x \rightarrow$ ___

8) $f(x) = -x^4 + x^2 + 6$

$f(x) \rightarrow$ ___, as $x \rightarrow$ ___
$f(x) \rightarrow$ ___, as $x \rightarrow$ ___

9) $f(x) = -x^3 + 2x^2 + 8$

$f(x) \rightarrow$ ___, as $x \rightarrow$ ___
$f(x) \rightarrow$ ___, as $x \rightarrow$ ___

10) $f(x) = x^4 - x^2 - 3$

$f(x) \rightarrow$ ___, as $x \rightarrow$ ___
$f(x) \rightarrow$ ___, as $x \rightarrow$ ___

11) $f(x) = -x^2 - 7x - 12$

$f(x) \rightarrow$ ___, as $x \rightarrow$ ___
$f(x) \rightarrow$ ___, as $x \rightarrow$ ___

12) $f(x) = -x^2 + 8x$

$f(x) \rightarrow$ ___, as $x \rightarrow$ ___
$f(x) \rightarrow$ ___, as $x \rightarrow$ ___

13) $f(x) = -x^5 + 4x^3 - 2x - 4$

$f(x) \rightarrow$ ___, as $x \rightarrow$ ___
$f(x) \rightarrow$ ___, as $x \rightarrow$ ___

14) $f(x) = x^3 + 10x^2 + 22x + 4$

$f(x) \rightarrow$ ___, as $x \rightarrow$ ___
$f(x) \rightarrow$ ___, as $x \rightarrow$ ___

Polynomial Division (Long Division)

✎ *Evaluate.*

1) $(x^2 - 3x + 4) \div (x - 1) =$

_____

2) $(x^2 + 6x + 8) \div (x - 2) =$

_____

3) $(x^2 + 6x - 5) \div (x + 3) =$

_____

4) $(x^2 - 4x + 12) \div (x - 2) =$

_____

5) $(x^2 + 2x - 36) \div (x - 5) =$

_____

6) $(x^2 + 32) \div (x + 2) =$

_____

7) $(2x^2 - x - 6) \div (x - 3) =$

_____

8) $(x^2 + x - 79) \div (x + 9) =$

_____

9) $(x^2 - x - 29) \div (x - 6) =$

_____

10) $(x^2 - 3x - 21) \div (x - 7) =$

_____

11) $(x^2 - 28) \div (x - 5) =$

_____

12) $(2x^2 - 15x - 36) \div (2x + 3) =$

_____

13) $(x^2 + 14x + 38) \div (x + 8) =$

_____

14) $(x^2 - 3x - 21) \div (x - 7) =$

_____

15) $(x^3 + 2x - 7x - 12) \div (x + 3) =$

_____

16) $(x^3 + 5x^2 + 10x + 6) \div (x + 1) =$

_____

17) $(x^3 + x^2 - 36x + 42) \div (x + 7) =$

_____

18) $(x^3 + 13x^2 + 42x + 54) \div (x + 9) =$

_____

19) $(x^5 - 5x^4 + 10x^2 - 42) \div (x - 5) =$

_____

20) $(x^3 - 2x^2 - 14x - 5) \div (x + 3) =$

_____

21) $(x^4 - 20x^3 + 93x + 71x) \div (x - 4) =$

_____

22) $(-x^4 + 4x^3 - 14x^3 + 14) \div (x - 2) =$

_____

Polynomial Division (Synthetic Division)

✎ *Evaluate.*

1) $(x^2 + 12) \div (x + 2) =$

2) $(x^2 + 5x + 15) \div (x + 5) =$

3) $(x^3 - 3x^2 - 9x) \div (x - 3) =$

4) $(3x^2 + 5x + 2) \div (x + 2) =$

5) $(7x^2 - 3x + 6) \div (x + 3) =$

6) $(4x^3 - 2x^2) \div (x + 2) =$

7) $(4x^2 + x + 1) \div (x - 1) =$

8) $(3x^2 - 4x + 2) \div (x - 2) =$

9) $(x^2 + 4x + 12) \div (x + 2) =$

10) $(x^3 - 20) \div (x - 3) =$

11) $(x^2 + 5x + 6) \div (x + 2) =$

12) $(x^3 - 3x^2 - 9x + 6) \div (x - 3) =$

13) $(3x^3 + 4x^2 - 2x - 4) \div (x + 2) =$

14) $(x^4 + 5x^3 - 6x + 3) \div (x + 3) =$

15) $(2x^3 - 5x^2 - 33x - 37) \div (x - 9) =$

16) $(x^4 + 2x^3 - 8x^2 - 9x) \div (x - 2) =$

17) $(5x^4 + 2x^2 - 15x + 12) \div (x + 2) =$

18) $(4x^3 - 49x^2 - 45x - 36) \div (x - 2) =$

19) $(x^3 - 13x^2 - 77x + 60) \div (x - 5) =$

20) $(x^3 - 13x^2 + 25x + 50) \div (x - 3) =$

21) $(x^3 - 11x^2 + 26x + 20) \div (x - 5) =$

22) $(x^3 + 15x^2 + 47x - 38) \div (x + 3) =$

23) $(x^3 - 3x^2 - 3x - 2) \div (x - 2) =$

24) $(x^4 - 6x^2 + 8x - 42) \div (x - 4) =$

Chapter 6: Polynomial Operations

Finding Zeros of Polynomials

✎ *Find the zeros of the Polynomials.*

1) $16x^2 - 4$

2) $25x^2 - 9$

3) $3x^2 + x - 5$

4) $x^2 - 2x - 6$

5) $3x^2 - 2x + 4$

6) $6x^2 + 13x - 15$

7) $5x^2 + 14x - 24$

8) $4x^2 - 8x - 16$

9) $x^3 + 5x^2 + 4x$

10) $x^3 - 2x^2 - 3x$

11) $x^3 + 5x^2 + 6x$

12) $x^3 + 8x^2 + 12x$

13) $x^3 - 4x$

14) $x^3 - 2x^2 - 3x + 6$

15) $x^3 + 3x^2 - x - 3$

16) $x^3 + x^2 - 8x - 6$

17) $x^3 - 3x^2 - 4x + 12$

18) $x^3 + 3x^2 - 10x$

19) $x^3 + 2x^2 - 5x - 6$

20) $x^3 - 4x^2 - 5x$

21) $x^4 - x^3 - 20x^2$

22) $x^3 + 4x^2 - 3x$

23) $x^4 - 14x^2 + 45$

24) $x^3 + 3x^2 - 14x - 20$

25) $x^4 - 10x^2 + 21$

26) $x^4 - 2x^2 - 2x - 4$

Polynomial Identities

✍ *Factorize the following expressions.*

1) $x^2 + 5xy + 4y^2$

2) $x^2 - xy - 6y^2$

3) $8x^2 - 10xy + 2y^2$

4) $3x^2 - 10xy - 8y^2$

5) $10x^2 - 13xy - 3y^2$

6) $18x^2 - 6xy - 4y^2$

7) $8x^3 + 12x^2 + 6x + 1$

8) $20x^2 + xy - 12y^2$

9) $2x^2 + 3xy - 2y^2$

10) $4x^2 - 10xy - 6y^2$

11) $8x^3 + 60x^2 + 150x + 125$

12) $8x^3 - 36x^2 + 54x - 27$

13) $27x^3 + 108x^2 + 144x + 64$

14) $-27x^3 - 54x^2 - 36x - 8$

15) $9x^2 + y^2 + 6xy + 2y + 6x + 1$

16) $-64x^3 + 96x^2 - 48x + 8$

17) $27x^3 + 27x^2 + 9x + 1$

18) $4x^2 + 4xy + 12x + y^2 + 6y + 9$

19) $125x^3 + 150x^2 + 60x + 8$

20) $8x^3 + 96x^2 + 384x + 512$

21) $64x^3 + 144x^2 + 108x + 27$

22) $9x^2 + 6xy + 6x + y^2 + 2y + 1$

23) $8x^3 + 12x^2y + 6xy^2 + y^3$

24) $27x^3 + 54x^2y + 36xy^2 + 8y^3$

25) $64x^3 - 144x^2y + 108xy^2 - 27y^3$

26) $4x^2 + 12xy + 9y^2 + 8x + 12y + 4$

Answers – Chapter 6

Writing Polynomials in Standard Form

1) $3x$

2) -3

3) $-4x^3 + 3x^2$

4) $4x^3$

5) $-7x^3 + 2x^2 + x$

6) $4x^3 - x^2$

7) $4x^3 - 2x^2 + 2x$

8) $-6x^3 - 2x^2 + 4x$

9) $2x^2 - 5x + 2$

10) $9x^4 - 7x + 12$

11) $-2x^3 + 5x^2 + 13x$

12) $-x^3 + 6x^2 + 10$

13) $9x^3 + 12x^2 - 7x$

14) $5x^4 - 2x^3 - 3x^2$

15) $-6x^4 + 3x^2 - 12$

16) $-9x^5 + 8x^3 + 5x^2 - 11$

17) $-2x^5 - 7x^4 + 4x^2 + 14$

18) $-5x^3 - x^2 - 2x$

19) $2x^5 + 11x^3 - 8x^2$

20) $-12x^4 + 5x^3 + 9x^2$

21) $-6x^4 + 29x^3 - 3x^2$

22) $-4x^4 + 12x^3 + 9x^2$

23) $-6x^3 + 6x^2 + 15x$

24) $11x^6 + 22x^4$

25) $15x^3 + 10x^2 + 5x$

26) $42x^4 - 7x^2 + 21x$

27) $-8x^5 + 6x^3 + 6x$

28) $24x^6 + 42x^4 - 12x$

29) $-12x^4 - 20x^3 + 24x^2$

30) $-18x^4 - 54x^2 + 27x$

31) $4x^4 + 6x^3 - 32x^2$

32) $6x^5 - 6x^4 - 84x^2$

Simplifying Polynomials

1) $8x - 40$

2) $6x^2 - 4x$

3) $15x^2 - 9x$

4) $14x^2 + 6x$

5) $32x^2 - 16x$

6) $30x^2 + 20x$

7) $2x^2 - 11x + 12$

8) $3x^2 - 11x - 20$

9) $x^2 - 8x + 15$

10) $9x^2 - 64$

11) $9x^2 - 36x + 32$

12) $-2x^3 + 6x^2$

13) $6x^3 - x^2 + 2x + 4$

14) $-9x^3 + 2x^2 + 5x$

15) $-3x^3 + 8x^2 - 9$

16) $2x^4 + 5x^3 - 7x^2$

17) $-4x^5 + 2x^4 - 6x^2$

18) $2x^4 - 3x^3 + 3x^2 - 2x$

19) $5x^4 - 2x^3 + 7x^2$

20) $6x^4 + 5x^3 - 3x^2$

21) $-10x^4 + 2x^3 - 8x^2 + 5x$

22) $-12x^3 - x^2 + 33$

23) $3x^3 + 2x^2 - 12x$

24) $-7x^3 - x^2 + 14$

25) $-x^3 + 8x^2$

26) $3x^3 - 1$

27) $-3x^4 - 12x^3$

28) $3x^6 - 162$

29) $-5x^3 + x^2 - x + 10$

30) $-5x^3 - x^2 + 18$

31) $16x^2 - 8x + 5$

32) $-7x^3 - x^2$

Adding and Subtracting Polynomials

1) $2x^2 + 1$

2) $4x^2 - 9$

3) $3x^2 - 6$

4) $4x^3 + 5x^2 - 8x$

5) $-3x^3 + 3x - 2$

6) $7x^3 + 8$

7) $11x^3 - 4$

8) $x^3 + 5x^2 - 6$

9) $3x$

10) $9x^2 + x - 2$

11) $9x^4 - 8x$

12) $-13x^3 - 4x$

13) $8x^3 - 14x^2 + 3x$

14) $-4x^3 + 14x^2 - 6$

15) $2x^4 + 11x^3$

16) $-6x^3 + 3x$

17) $-13x^4 + 5x$

18) $-7x^4 + 8x$

19) $14x^3 - 4x^2 - 7$

20) $-5x^4 + 12x^3$

Multiplying and Dividing Monomials

1) $6x^7$

2) $12x^9$

3) $-14x^{14}$

4) $-35x^{13}y^{15}$

5) $24x^7y^{11}$

6) $56y^6x^5$

7) $8x^4y^4$

8) $18x^{15}y^{12}$

9) $30x^{12}y^7$

10) $-56x^{12}y^4$

11) $54x^{13}y^6$

12) $48x^{14}y^9$

13) $-35x^{15}y^{17}$

14) $30x^5y^7$

15) $36x^{12}y^{21}$

16) $-20x^{21}y^{13}$

17) $6x^4y$

18) $3x^2y^5$

19) $4x^3y^5$

Effortless Math Education

Multiplying a Polynomial and a Monomial

1) $x^2 - 5x$

2) $2x + 6$

3) $x^2 - 7x$

4) $x^2 + 9x$

5) $2x^2 - 4x$

6) $20x + 15$

7) $12x^2 - 16x$

8) $5x^2 + 2xy$

9) $3x^2 - 6xy$

10) $18x^2 - 24xy$

11) $6x^2 - 16x$

12) $24x^2 - 36xy$

13) $12x^2 - 6xy$

14) $4x^2 - 12xy$

15) $5x^3 + 5xy^2$

16) $6x^3 - 3xy^2$

17) $54x^2 + 18y^2$

18) $-12x^3y + 8xy$

19) $-18x^2 + 15xy - 9$

20) $6x^2 - 24xy - 18$

Multiplying Binomials

1) $x^2 + x - 12$

2) $x^2 + 8x + 15$

3) $x^2 - 13x + 42$

4) $x^2 - 13x + 36$

5) $x^2 - 12x + 35$

6) $x^2 + 8x + 12$

7) $x^2 - 6x - 27$

8) $x^2 - 13x + 40$

9) $x^2 + 10x + 21$

10) $x^2 - 5x - 36$

11) $x^2 + 12x + 36$

12) $x^2 + 14x + 49$

13) $x^2 - x - 56$

14) $x^2 + 18x + 81$

15) $x^2 - 16x + 64$

16) $x^2 - 4x - 45$

17) $2x^2 + 3x - 20$

18) $2x^2 + 12x + 18$

19) $2x^2 + 14x + 20$

20) $4x^2 - 2x - 6$

Factoring Trinomials

1) $(x + 4)(x + 1)$

2) $(x + 3)(x + 2)$

3) $(x - 1)(x - 3)$

4) $(x - 5)(x - 5)$

5) $(x - 8)(x - 5)$

6) $(x + 6)(x + 2)$

7) $(x - 9)(x + 3)$

8) $(x - 8)(x - 6)$

9) $(x + 8)(x + 7)$

10) $(x - 9)(x + 4)$

11) $(x + 6)(x + 6)$

12) $(x + 7)(x + 9)$

13) $(x - 8)(x + 9)$

14) $(x + 9)(x + 9)$

15) $(x - 8)(x - 8)$

16) $(x - 9)(x - 9)$

17) $2(x + 1)(x + 4)$

18) $2(x - 1)(x + 3)$

19) $(2x + 1)(x + 4)$

20) $4(x - 2)(x + 3)$

Operations with Polynomials

1) $6x + 4$

2) $-6x - 15$

3) $28x - 12$

4) $10x - 20$

5) $6x^2 - 21x$

6) $-6x^2 - 8x$

7) $16x^2 - 24x$

8) $3x^3 + 4x^2$

9) $x^4 + 5x^3$

10) $5x^5 - 3x^4$

11) $54x + 18$

12) $24x + 56$

13) $30x - 5$

14) $-24x + 9$

15) $18x^3 - 15x^2$

16) $35x^3 - 10x^2$

17) $-18x^4 + 24x^3$

18) $-14x^5 + 28x^4$

19) $8x^2 + 16x - 24$

20) $16x^2 - 8x + 4$

21) $6x^2 + 4x - 4$

22) $40x^3 + 24x^2 + 64x$

23) $27x^2 - 6x - 1$

24) $24x^2 + 10x - 25$

25) $35x^2 - 27x - 18$

26) $9x^2 + 12x - 32$

End Behavior of Polynomial Functions

1) $f(x) \to +\infty$, as $x \to -\infty$
   $f(x) \to +\infty$, as $x \to +\infty$

2) $f(x) \to -\infty$, as $x \to -\infty$
   $f(x) \to -\infty$, as $x \to +\infty$

3) $f(x) \to -\infty$, as $x \to -\infty$
   $f(x) \to +\infty$, as $x \to +\infty$

4) $f(x) \to +\infty$, as $x \to -\infty$
   $f(x) \to -\infty$, as $x \to +\infty$

5) $f(x) \to +\infty$, as $x \to -\infty$
   $f(x) \to +\infty$, as $x \to +\infty$

6) $f(x) \to -\infty$, as $x \to -\infty$
   $f(x) \to +\infty$, as $x \to +\infty$

7) $f(x) \to -\infty$, as $x \to -\infty$
   $f(x) \to +\infty$, as $x \to +\infty$

8) $f(x) \to -\infty$, as $x \to -\infty$
   $f(x) \to -\infty$, as $x \to +\infty$

9) $f(x) \to +\infty$, as $x \to -\infty$
   $f(x) \to -\infty$, as $x \to +\infty$

10) $f(x) \to +\infty$, as $x \to -\infty$
    $f(x) \to +\infty$, as $x \to +\infty$

11) $f(x) \to -\infty$, as $x \to -\infty$
    $f(x) \to -\infty$, as $x \to +\infty$

12) $f(x) \to -\infty$, as $x \to -\infty$
    $f(x) \to -\infty$, as $x \to +\infty$

13) $f(x) \to +\infty$, as $x \to -\infty$
    $f(x) \to -\infty$, as $x \to +\infty$

14) $f(x) \to -\infty$, as $x \to -\infty$
    $f(x) \to +\infty$, as $x \to +\infty$

Polynomial Division (Long Division)

1) $x - 2 + \frac{2}{x-1}$

2) $x + 8 + \frac{24}{x-2}$

3) $x + 3 - \frac{14}{x+3}$

4) $x - 2 + \frac{8}{x-2}$

5) $x + 7 - \frac{1}{x-5}$

6) $x - 2 + \frac{36}{x+2}$

7) $2x + 5 + \frac{9}{x-3}$

8) $x - 8 - \frac{7}{x+9}$

9) $x + 5 + \frac{1}{x-6}$

10) $x + 4 + \frac{7}{x-7}$

11) $x + 5 - \frac{3}{x-5}$

12) $x - 9 - \frac{9}{2x+3}$

13) $x + 6 - \frac{10}{x+8}$

14) $x + 4 + \frac{7}{x-7}$

15) $x^2 - 3x + 4 - \frac{24}{x+3}$

16) $x^2 + 4x + 6$

17) $x^2 - 6x + 6$

18) $x^2 + 4x + 6$

19) $x^4 + 10x + 50 + \frac{208}{x-5}$

20) $x^2 - 5x + 1 - \frac{8}{x+3}$

21) $x^3 - 16x^2 - 64x - 92 - \frac{368}{x-4}$

22) $-x^3 - 12x^2 - 24x - 48 - \frac{82}{x-2}$

Polynomial Division (Synthetic Division)

1) $x - 2 + \frac{16}{x+2}$

2) $x + \frac{15}{x+5}$

3) $x^2 - 9 - \frac{27}{x-3}$

4) $3x - 1 + \frac{4}{x+2}$

5) $7x - 24 + \frac{78}{x+3}$

6) $4x^2 - 10x + 20 - \frac{40}{x+2}$

7) $4x + 5 + \frac{6}{x-1}$

8) $3x + 2 + \frac{6}{x-2}$

9) $x + 2 + \frac{8}{x+2}$

10) $x^2 + 3x + 9 + \frac{7}{x-3}$

11) $x + 3$

12) $x^2 - 9 - \frac{21}{x-3}$

13) $3x^2 - 2x + 2 - \frac{8}{x+2}$

14) $x^3 + 2x^2 - 6x + 12 - \frac{33}{x+3}$

15) $2x^2 + 13x + 84 + \frac{719}{x-9}$

16) $x^3 + 4x^2 - 9 - \frac{18}{x-2}$

17) $5x^3 - 10x^2 + 22x - 59 + \frac{130}{x+2}$

18) $4x^2 - 41x - 127 - \frac{290}{x-2}$

19) $x^2 - 8x - 117 - \frac{525}{x-5}$

20) $x^2 - 10x - 5 + \frac{35}{x-3}$

21) $x^2 - 6x - 4$

22) $x^2 + 12x + 11 - \frac{71}{x+3}$

23) $x^2 - x - 5 - \frac{12}{x-2}$

24) $x^3 + 4x^2 + 10x + 48 + \frac{150}{x-4}$

Finding Zeros of Polynomials

1) $\frac{1}{2}, -\frac{1}{2}$

2) $\frac{3}{5}, -\frac{3}{5}$

3) $\frac{-1+\sqrt{61}}{6}, \frac{-1-\sqrt{61}}{6}$

4) $1 + \sqrt{7}, 1 - \sqrt{7}$

5) $\frac{1}{3} + i\frac{\sqrt{11}}{3}, \frac{1}{3} - i\frac{\sqrt{11}}{3}$

6) $\frac{5}{6}, -3$

7) $-4, \frac{6}{5}$

8) $1 + \sqrt{5}, 1 - \sqrt{5}$

9) $0, -1, -4$

10) $0, 3, -1$

11) $0, -2, -3$

12) $0, -2, -6$

13) $0, 2, -2$

14) $2, \sqrt{3}, -\sqrt{3}$

15) $-3, 1, -1$

16) $-3, 1 + \sqrt{3}, 1 - \sqrt{3}$

17) $3, 2, -2$

18) $0, 2, -5$

19) $-3, -1, 2$

20) $5, -1, 0$

21) $0, -4, 5$

22) $0, -2 + \sqrt{7}, -2 - \sqrt{7}$

23) $\sqrt{5}, -\sqrt{5}, 3, -3$

24) $-5, 1 + \sqrt{5}, 1 - \sqrt{5}$

25) $\sqrt{3}, -\sqrt{3}, \sqrt{7}, -\sqrt{7}$

26) $2, -1.54$

Polynomial Identities

1) $(x + y)(x + 4y)$

2) $(x - 3y)(x + 2y)$

3) $2(4x - y)(x - y)$

4) $(3x + 2y)(x - 4y)$

5) $(5x + y)(2x - 3y)$

6) $2(3x + y)(3x - 2y)$

7) $(2x + 1)^3$

8) $(5x + 4y)(4x - 3y)$

9) $(2x - y)(x + 2y)$

10) $2(2x + y)(x - 3y)$

11) $(2x + 5)^3$

12) $(2x - 3)^3$

13) $(3x + 4)^3$

14) $(-3x + 2)^3$

15) $(3x + y + 1)^2$

16) $-8(2x - 1)^3$

17) $(3x + 1)^3$

18) $(2x + y + 3)^2$

19) $(5x + 2)^3$

20) $8(x + 4)^3$

21) $(4x + 3)^3$

22) $(3x + y + 1)^2$

23) $(2x + y)^3$

24) $(3x + 2y)^3$

25) $(4x - 3y)^3$

26) $(2x + 3y + 2)^2$

Chapter 7: Functions Operations

Math Topics that you'll learn in this Chapter:

- ✓ Function Notation
- ✓ Adding and Subtracting Functions
- ✓ Multiplying and Dividing Functions
- ✓ Composition of Functions
- ✓ Function Inverses
- ✓ Domain and Range of Function
- ✓ Piecewise Function
- ✓ Positive, Negative, Increasing, and Decreasing Functions on Intervals
- ✓ Average rate of change word problems

71

Chapter 7: Functions Operations

Function Notation

✎ *Evaluate each function.*

1) $f(x) = x - 3$, find $f(-2)$

_____

2) $g(x) = x + 5$, find $g(6)$

_____

3) $h(x) = x + 8$, find $h(2)$

_____

4) $f(x) = -x - 7$, find $f(5)$

_____

5) $f(x) = 2x - 7$, find $f(-1)$

_____

6) $w(x) = -2 - 4x$, find $w(5)$

_____

7) $g(n) = 6n - 3$, find $g(-2)$

_____

8) $h(x) = -8x + 12$, find $h(3)$

_____

9) $k(n) = 14 - 3n$, find $k(3)$

_____

10) $g(x) = 4x - 4$, find $g(-2)$

_____

11) $k(n) = 8n - 7$, find $k(4)$

_____

12) $w(n) = -2n + 14$, find $w(5)$

_____

13) $h(x) = 5x - 18$, find $h(8)$

_____

14) $g(n) = 2n^2 + 2$, find $g(5)$

_____

15) $f(x) = 3x^2 - 13$, find $f(2)$

_____

16) $g(n) = 5n^2 + 7$, find $g(-3)$

_____

17) $h(n) = 5n^2 - 10$, find $h(4)$

_____

18) $g(x) = -3x^2 - 6x$, find $g(2)$

_____

19) $k(n) = 4n^3 + n$, find $k(-5)$

_____

20) $f(x) = -3x + 10$, find $f(3x)$

_____

21) $k(a) = 4a + 9$, find $k(a - 1)$

_____

22) $h(x) = 8x + 4$, find $h(5x)$

_____

Chapter 7: Functions Operations

Adding and Subtracting Functions

✍ *Perform the indicated operation.*

1) $f(x) = x + 4$

   $g(x) = 2x + 5$

   Find $(f - g)(2)$

   _____

2) $g(x) = x - 2$

   $f(x) = -x - 6$

   Find $(g - f)(-2)$

   _____

3) $h(t) = 4t + 4$

   $g(t) = 3t + 2$

   Find $(h + g)(-1)$

   _____

4) $g(a) = 5a - 7$

   $f(a) = a^2 + 3$

   Find $(g + f)(2)$

   _____

5) $g(x) = 4x - 5$

   $f(x) = 6x^2 + 5$

   Find $(g - f)(-2)$

   _____

6) $h(x) = x^2 + 3$

   $g(x) = -4x + 1$

   Find $(h + g)(4)$

   _____

7) $f(x) = -3x - 9$

   $g(x) = x^2 + 5$

   Find $(f - g)(6)$

   _____

8) $h(n) = -4n^2 + 9$

   $g(n) = 5n + 6$

   Find $(h - g)(5)$

   _____

9) $g(x) = 4x^2 - 3x - 1$

   $f(x) = 6x + 10$

   Find $(g - f)(a)$

   _____

10) $g(t) = -6t - 7$

    $f(t) = -t^2 + 3t + 15$

    Find $(g + f)(t)$

    _____

Multiplying and Dividing Functions

✎ *Perform the indicated operation.*

1) $g(x) = x + 6$

$f(x) = x + 4$

Find $(g.f)(2)$

_____

2) $f(x) = 3x$

$h(x) = -x + 5$

Find $(f.h)(-2)$

_____

3) $g(a) = a + 5$

$h(a) = 2a - 4$

Find $(g.h)(4)$

_____

4) $f(x) = 3x + 2$

$h(x) = 2x - 3$

Find $(\frac{f}{h})(2)$

_____

5) $f(a) = a^2 - 2$

$g(a) = -4 + 3a$

Find $(\frac{f}{g})(2)$

_____

6) $g(a) = 4a + 6$

$f(a) = 2a - 8$

Find $(\frac{g}{f})(3)$

_____

7) $g(t) = t^2 + 6$

$h(t) = 2t - 3$

Find $(g.h)(-3)$

_____

8) $g(x) = x^2 + 3x + 4$

$h(x) = 2x + 6$

Find $(g.h)(2)$

_____

9) $g(a) = 2a^2 - 5a + 1$

$f(a) = 2a^3 - 6$

Find $(\frac{g}{f})(4)$

_____

10) $g(x) = -3x^2 + 4 - 2x$

$f(x) = x^2 - 5$

Find $(g.f)(3)$

_____

Composition of Functions

✎ *Using $f(x) = x + 6$ and $g(x) = 3x$, find:*

1) $f\big(g(1)\big) = $ ____

2) $f\big(g(-1)\big) = $ ____

3) $g\big(f(-3)\big) = $ ____

4) $g\big(f(4)\big) = $ ____

5) $f\big(g(2)\big) = $ ____

6) $g\big(f(3)\big) = $ ____

✎ *Using $f(x) = 2x + 5$ and $g(x) = x - 2$, find:*

7) $g\big(f(2)\big) = $ ____

8) $g\big(f(-2)\big) = $ ____

9) $f\big(g(5)\big) = $ ____

10) $f\big(f(4)\big) = $ ____

11) $g\big(f(3)\big) = $ ____

12) $g\big(f(-3)\big) = $ ____

✎ *Using $f(x) = 4x - 2$ and $g(x) = x - 5$, find:*

13) $g\big(f(-2)\big) = $ ____

14) $f\big(f(4)\big) = $ ____

15) $f\big(g(5)\big) = $ ____

16) $f\big(f(3)\big) = $ ____

17) $g\big(f(-3)\big) = $ ____

18) $g\big(g(6)\big) = $ ____

✎ *Using $f(x) = 6x + 2$ and $g(x) = 2x - 3$, find:*

19) $f\big(g(-3)\big) = $ ____

20) $g\big(f(5)\big) = $ ____

21) $f\big(g(4)\big) = $ ____

22) $f\big(f(3)\big) = $ ____

Function Inverses

✎ *Find the inverse of each function.*

1) $g(x) = 6x \rightarrow g^{-1}(x) =$

2) $h(x) = \frac{1}{x-1} \rightarrow h^{-1}(x) =$

3) $g(x) = 12x \rightarrow g^{-1}(x) =$

4) $f(x) = \frac{1}{x} - 6 \rightarrow f^{-1}(x) =$

5) $h(x) = \frac{1}{x+4} \rightarrow h^{-1}(x) =$

6) $g(x) = \frac{7}{-x-3} \rightarrow g^{-1}(x) =$

7) $h(x) = \frac{x+9}{3} \rightarrow h^{-1}(x) =$

8) $h(x) = \frac{2x-10}{4} \rightarrow h^{-1}(x) =$

9) $f(x) = \frac{-15+x}{3} \rightarrow f^{-1}(x) =$

10) $s(x) = \sqrt{x} - 2 \rightarrow s^{-1}(x) =$

11) $h(x) = \frac{4}{x+2} \rightarrow h^{-1}(x) =$

12) $f(x) = (x-3)^3 \rightarrow f^{-1}(x) =$

13) $s(x) = -2x + 5 \rightarrow s^{-1}(x) =$

14) $k(x) = \frac{3}{-x-2} \rightarrow k^{-1}(x) =$

15) $f(x) = \sqrt[3]{x} - 3 \rightarrow f^{-1}(x) =$

16) $f(x) = \frac{1}{x} - 2 \rightarrow f^{-1}(x) =$

17) $s(x) = -3x + 1 \rightarrow s^{-1}(x) =$

18) $k(x) = x + 5 \rightarrow k^{-1}(x) =$

19) $h(x) = \frac{5x+16}{2} \rightarrow h^{-1}(x) =$

20) $g(x) = -x + 6 \rightarrow g^{-1}(x) =$

21) $h(x) = \frac{-x-5}{3} \rightarrow h^{-1}(x) =$

22) $w(x) = \frac{2}{7}x - \frac{10}{7} \rightarrow w^{-1}(x) =$

Domain and Range of Function

✎ *Find the domain and range of the functions.*

1) $x^3 - 4$

Domain: _____

Range: _____

2) $\sqrt{x-8} + 4$

Domain: _____

Range: _____

3) $\dfrac{2}{2x-1}$

Domain: _____

Range: _____

4) $-2x^3 + 6$

Domain: _____

Range: _____

5) $x^2 + 3x$

Domain: _____

Range: _____

6) $\dfrac{x}{x+2}$

Domain: _____

Range: _____

7) $-2(x+1)^2 + 5$

Domain: _____

Range: _____

8) $8x^3 + 2x$

Domain: _____

Range: _____

9) $\sqrt{x+2} - 6$

Domain: _____

Range: _____

10) $\dfrac{x^2}{3x+2}$

Domain: _____

Range: _____

11) $-2x^2 + 4x + 8$

Domain: _____

Range: _____

12) $\sqrt{3x^2 + 5} - 2$

Domain: _____

Range: _____

13) $-6x^3 + 5x^2 - 4$

Domain: _____

Range: _____

14) $\dfrac{3x^3}{2x-1}$

Domain: _____

Range: _____

Piecewise Function

✍ *Graph.*

1) $f(x) = \begin{cases} 2 + x, \ x < -1 \\ x - 1, \ x \geq 0 \end{cases}$

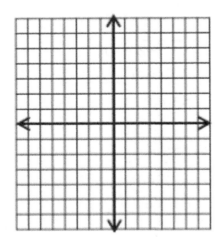

2) $f(x) = \begin{cases} 3 - x, \ -2 < x < 2 \\ 2x \quad, \ -1 < x < 3 \end{cases}$

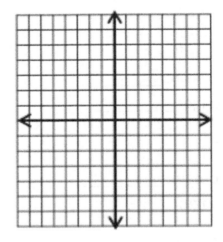

3) $f(x) = \begin{cases} x + 2 \ , 0 \leq x < 4 \\ -x - 1, \ 1 < x < 4 \end{cases}$

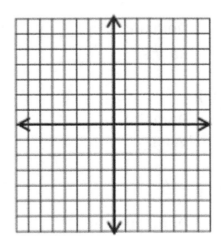

4) $f(x) = \begin{cases} -2x \quad, \ -1 \leq x \leq 3 \\ 3x - 1, \ -2 < x < 2 \end{cases}$

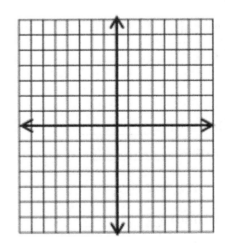

Positive, Negative, Increasing, and Decreasing Functions on Intervals

✍ *Determine the intervals where the function is increasing and decreasing.*

Submit your solution in interval notation.

1) $2x^2 + 1$

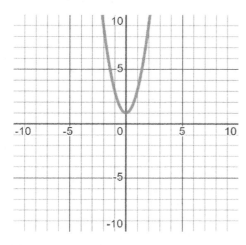

2) $-x^3 - 2$

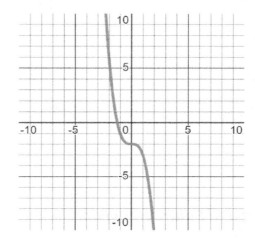

3) $(x - 1)^2 + 2$

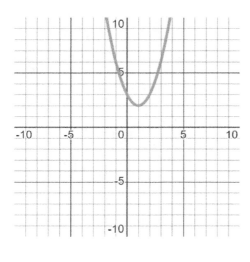

4) $x^3 - 2x^2 - 5$

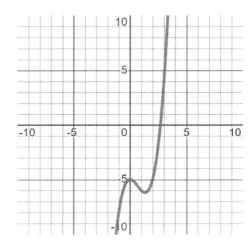

Answers – Chapter 7

Function Notation

1) -5

2) 11

3) 10

4) -12

5) -9

6) -22

7) -15

8) -12

9) 5

10) -12

11) 25

12) 4

13) 22

14) 52

15) -1

16) 52

17) 70

18) -24

19) -505

20) $-9x + 10$

21) $4a + 5$

22) $40x + 4$

Adding and Subtracting Functions

1) -3

2) 0

3) -1

4) 10

5) -42

6) 4

7) -68

8) -122

9) $4a^2 - 9a - 11$

10) $-t^2 - 3t + 8$

Multiplying and Dividing Functions

1) 48

2) -42

3) 36

4) 8

5) 1

6) -9

7) -135

8) 140

9) $\frac{13}{122}$

10) -116

Composition of Functions

1) $f(g(1)) = 9$

2) $f(g(-1)) = 3$

3) $g(f(-3)) = 9$

4) $g(f(4)) = 30$

5) $f(g(2)) = 12$

6) $g(f(3)) = 27$

7) $g(f(2)) = 7$

8) $g(f(-2)) = -1$

9) $f(g(5)) = 11$

10) $f(f(4)) = 31$

11) $g(f(3)) = 9$

12) $g(f(-3)) = -3$

13) $g(f(-2)) = -15$

14) $f(f(4)) = 54$

15) $f(g(5)) = -2$

16) $f(f(3)) = 38$

17) $g(f(-3)) = -19$

18) $g(g(6)) = -4$

19) $f(g(-3)) = -52$

20) $g(f(5)) = 61$

21) $f(g(4)) = 32$

22) $f(f(3)) = 122$

Function Inverses

1) $g^{-1}(x) = \frac{x}{6}$

2) $h^{-1}(x) = \frac{1}{x} + 1$

3) $g^{-1}(x) = \frac{x}{12}$

4) $f^{-1}(x) = \frac{1}{x+6}$

5) $h^{-1}(x) = \frac{1}{x} - 4$

6) $g^{-1}(x) = -\frac{7+3x}{x}$

7) $h^{-1}(x) = 3x - 9$

8) $h^{-1}(x) = 2x + 5$

9) $f^{-1}(x) = 3x + 15$

10) $s^{-1}(x) = x^2 + 4x + 4$

11) $h^{-1}(x) = \frac{4-2x}{x}$

12) $f^{-1}(x) = \sqrt[3]{x} + 3$

13) $s^{-1}(x) = -\frac{1}{2}x + \frac{5}{2}$

14) $k^{-1}(x) = -\frac{3}{x} - 2$

15) $f^{-1}(x) = (x + 3)^3$

16) $f^{-1}(x) = \frac{1}{x+2}$

17) $s^{-1}(x) = -\frac{1}{3}x + \frac{1}{3}$

18) $k^{-1}(x) = x - 5$

19) $h^{-1}(x) = \frac{2x-16}{5}$

20) $g^{-1}(x) = -x + 6$

21) $h^{-1}(x) = -3x - 5$

22) $w^{-1}(x) = 5 + \frac{7}{2}x$

Domain and Range of Function

1) Domain: $-\infty < x < \infty$

   Range: $-\infty < f(x) < \infty$

2) Domain: $x \geq 8$

   Range: $f(x) \geq 4$

3) Domain: $x < \frac{1}{2}$ or $x > \frac{1}{2}$

   Range: $f(x) < 0$ or $f(x) > 0$

4) Domain: $-\infty < x < \infty$

   Range: $-\infty < f(x) < \infty$

5) Domain: $-\infty < x < \infty$

   Range: $f(x) \geq -\frac{9}{4}$

6) Domain: $x < -2$ or $x > -2$

   Range: $f(x) < 1$ or $f(x) > 1$

7) Domain: $-\infty < x < \infty$

   Range: $f(x) \leq 5$

8) Domain: $-\infty < x < \infty$

   Range: $-\infty < f(x) < \infty$

9) Domain: $x \geq -2$

   Range: $f(x) \geq -6$

10) Domain: $x < -\frac{2}{3}$ or $x > -\frac{2}{3}$

    Range: $f(x) \leq -\frac{8}{9}$ or $f(x) \geq 0$

11) Domain: $-\infty < x < \infty$

    Range: $f(x) \leq 10$

12) Domain: $-\infty < x < \infty$

    Range: $f(x) \geq \sqrt{5} - 2$

13) Domain: $-\infty < x < \infty$

    Range: $-\infty < f(x) < \infty$

14) Domain: $x < \frac{1}{2}$ or $x > \frac{1}{2}$

    Range: $-\infty < f(x) < \infty$

Piecewise Function

1) $f(x) = \begin{cases} 2 + x, & x < -1 \\ x - 1, & x \geq 0 \end{cases}$

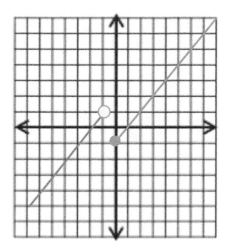

2) $f(x) = \begin{cases} 3 - x, & -2 < x < 2 \\ 2x, & -1 < x < 3 \end{cases}$

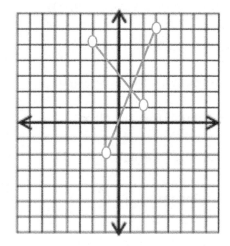

3) $f(x) = \begin{cases} x + 2, & 0 \leq x < 4 \\ -x - 1, & 1 < x < 4 \end{cases}$

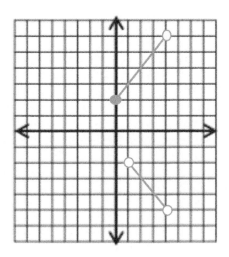

4) $f(x) = \begin{cases} -2x, & -1 \leq x \leq 3 \\ 3x - 1, & -2 < x < 2 \end{cases}$

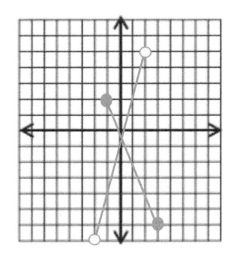

Positive, Negative, Increasing and Decreasing Functions on Intervals.

1) Increasing intervals: $(0, \infty)$

   Decreasing intervals: $(-\infty, 0)$

2) Decreasing intervals: $(0, \infty)$

   Decreasing intervals: $(-\infty, 0)$

3) Increasing intervals: $(1, \infty)$

   Decreasing intervals: $(-\infty, 1)$

4) Increasing intervals: $(\frac{4}{3}, \infty)$

   Decreasing intervals: $(0, \frac{4}{3})$

   Increasing intervals: $(-\infty, 0)$

Chapter 8:
Exponential
Functions

Math Topics that you'll learn in this Chapter:

- ✓ Exponential Function
- ✓ Linear, Quadratic and Exponential Models
- ✓ Linear vs Exponential Growth

Exponential Function

✎ *Sketch the graph of each function.*

1) $2 \cdot \left(\frac{1}{3}\right)^x$

2) $5 \cdot (2)^x$

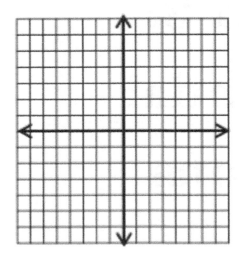

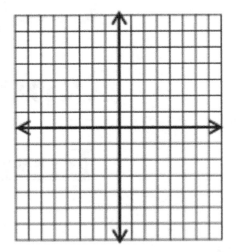

3) $\frac{1}{2} \cdot (4)^x$

4) $-\frac{1}{3} \cdot \left(\frac{1}{2}\right)^x$

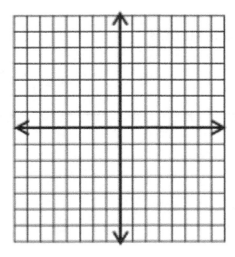

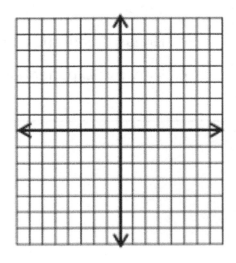

Linear, Quadratic and Exponential Models

✎ *Identify the following equations as linear, quadratic, or exponential.*

1) $x^2 - 3x + 5$ _____

2) $2^x + 1$ _____

3) $2x - 9$ _____

4) $-6(2)^x$ _____

5) $(x - 1)^2 - 3$ _____

6) $-5x + 1$ _____

7) $4 - \frac{2}{3}x$ _____

8) $8(\frac{1}{2})^x$ _____

✎ *Determine whether the following table of values represents a linear function, an exponential function, or a quadratic function.*

9) _____

x	-2	-1	0	1	2
y	$\frac{1}{2}$	1	2	4	8

10) _____

x	-2	-1	0	1	2
y	5	2	1	2	5

11) _____

x	-2	-1	0	1	2
y	-4	-1	2	5	8

Linear vs Exponential Growth

✎ *Using the data in this table, determine whether this relationship is linear, exponential, or neither.*

1) _____

x	-2	-1	0	1	2
y	-6	-3	0	3	6

2) _____

x	-2	-1	0	1	2
y	$\frac{1}{9}$	$\frac{1}{3}$	1	3	9

3) _____

x	-2	-1	0	1	2
y	1	-2	-3	-2	1

4) _____

x	-2	-1	0	1	2
y	$-\frac{3}{4}$	$-\frac{1}{2}$	1	1	3

5) _____

x	-2	-1	0	1	2
y	-8	-6	-4	-2	0

Effortless Math Education

Answers – Chapter 8

Exponential Function

1) $2 \cdot \left(\frac{1}{3}\right)^x$

2) $5 \cdot (2)^x$

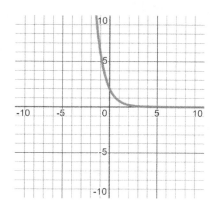

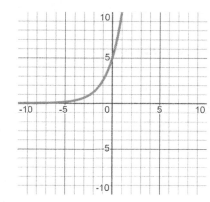

3) $\frac{1}{2} \cdot (4)^x$

4) $-\frac{1}{3} \cdot \left(\frac{1}{2}\right)^x$

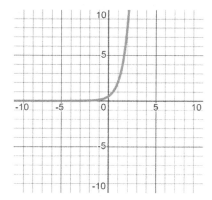

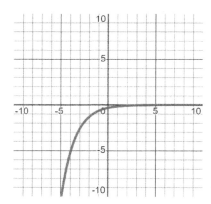

Linear, Quadratic and Exponential Models

1) Quadratic

2) Exponential

3) Linear

4) Exponential

5) Quadratic

6) Linear

7) Linear

8) Exponential

9) Exponential

10) Quadratic

11) Linear

Linear vs Exponential Growth

1) $y = 3x$, Linear

2) $(3)^x$, exponential

3) $y = x^2 - 3$, Quadratic

4) $2^x - 1$, exponential

5) $y = 2x - 4$, Linear

Chapter 9:
Logarithms

Math Topics that you'll learn in this Chapter:

- ✓ Evaluating Logarithms
- ✓ Properties of Logarithms
- ✓ Natural Logarithms
- ✓ Solving Logarithmic Equations

Evaluating Logarithms

✎ *Evaluate each logarithm.*

1) $log_2 4 =$

2) $log_2 8 =$

3) $log_3 27 =$

4) $log_3 9 =$

5) $log_4 16 =$

6) $log_2 32 =$

7) $log_8 64 =$

8) $log_2 \frac{1}{2} =$

9) $log_2 \frac{1}{8} =$

10) $log_3 \frac{1}{3} =$

11) $log_4 \frac{1}{16} =$

12) $log_3 \frac{1}{9} =$

13) $log_7 \frac{1}{49} =$

14) $log_{64} \frac{1}{4} =$

15) $log_{625} 5 =$

16) $log_2 \frac{1}{64} =$

17) $log_4 \frac{1}{64} =$

18) $log_{36} \frac{1}{6} =$

✎ *Circle the points which are on the graph of the given logarithmic functions.*

19) $y = 2 \, log_3(x + 1) + 2$ $(2, 4),$ $(8, 4),$ $(0, 3)$

20) $y = 3 \, log_3(3x) - 2$ $(3, 6),$ $(3, 4),$ $(\frac{1}{3}, 2)$

21) $y = -2 \, log_2 2(x + 1) + 1$ $(3, -3),$ $(2, 1),$ $(5, 5)$

22) $y = 4 \, log_4(4x) + 7$ $(1, 7),$ $(1, 11),$ $(4, 8)$

23) $y = - \, log_2 2(x + 3) + 1$ $(-2, 0),$ $(1, 2),$ $(5, 3)$

24) $y = - \, log_5(x - 3) + 8$ $(4, 8),$ $(8, 8),$ $(4, 4)$

25) $y = 3 \, log_4(x + 1) + 3$ $(3, 3),$ $(3, 6),$ $(0, 4)$

Chapter 9: Logarithms

Properties of Logarithms

✎ *Expand each logarithm.*

1) $log(8 \times 5) =$

2) $log(9 \times 4) =$

3) $log(3 \times 7) =$

4) $log(\frac{3}{4}) =$

5) $log(\frac{5}{7}) =$

6) $log(\frac{2}{5})^3 =$

7) $log(2 \times 3^4) =$

8) $log(\frac{5}{7})^4 =$

9) $log(\frac{2^3}{7}) \, log\left(\frac{2^3}{7}\right) =$

10) $log(x \times y)^5 =$

11) $log(x^3 \times y \times z^4) =$

12) $log(\frac{u^4}{v}) \, log\left(\frac{u^4}{v}\right) =$

13) $log(\frac{x}{y^6}) =$

✎ *Condense each expression to a single logarithm.*

14) $log\,2 - log\,9 =$

15) $log\,5 + log\,3 =$

16) $5\,log\,6 - 3\,log\,4 =$

17) $4\,log\,7 - 2\,log\,9 =$

18) $3\,log\,5 - log\,14 =$

19) $7\,log\,3 - 4\,log\,4 =$

20) $log\,7 - 2\,log\,12 =$

21) $2\,log\,5 + 3\,log\,8 =$

22) $4\,log\,3 + 5\,log\,7 =$

23) $4\,log_5\,a + 7\,log_5\,b =$

24) $2\,log_3\,x - 9\,log_3\,y =$

25) $log_4\,u - 6\,log_4\,v =$

26) $4\,log_6\,u + 8\,log_6\,v =$

27) $4\,log_3\,u - 20\,log_3\,v =$

Natural Logarithms

✎ *Solve each equation for x.*

1) $e^x = 3$

2) $e^x = 4$

3) $e^x = 8$

4) $\ln x = 6$

5) $\ln(\ln x) = 5$

6) $e^x = 9$

7) $\ln(2x + 5) = 4$

8) $\ln(2x - 1) = 1$

9) $\ln(6x - 1) = 1$

10) $\ln x = \frac{1}{2}$

11) $\ln 2x = e^2$

12) $\ln x = \ln 4 + \ln 7$

13) $\ln x = 2 \ln 4 + \ln 5$

✎ *Evaluate each expression without using a calculator.*

14) $\ln 1 =$

15) $\ln e^3 =$

16) $2 \ln e =$

17) $\ln e^2 =$

18) $4 \ln e =$

19) $\ln(\frac{1}{e}) =$

20) $e^{\ln 10} =$

21) $e^{3 \ln 2} =$

22) $e^{5 \ln 2} =$

23) $\ln \sqrt{e} =$

✎ *Simplify the following expressions to simplest form.*

24) $e^{-2 \ln 5 + 2 \ln 3} =$

25) $e^{-\ln(\frac{1}{e})} =$

26) $2 \ln(e^3) =$

27) $\ln(\frac{1}{e})^2 =$

28) $e^{\ln 2 + 3 \ln 2} =$

29) $e^{\ln(\frac{2}{e})} =$

30) $5 \ln(1^{-e}) =$

31) $\ln(\frac{1}{e})^{-3} =$

32) $\ln(\frac{\sqrt{e}}{e}) =$

33) $e^{-2 \ln e + 2 \ln 2} =$

34) $e^{\ln\frac{1}{e}} =$

35) $3 \ln(e^e) =$

Chapter 9: Logarithms

Solving Logarithmic Equations

✎ *Find the value of the variables in each equation.*

1) $2 \log_7 49 - 2x = 0$

2) $-\log_5 7x = 2$

3) $\log x + 5 = 2$

4) $\log x - \log 4 = 3$

5) $\log x + \log 2 = 4$

6) $\log 10 + \log x = 1$

7) $\log x + \log 8 = \log 48$

8) $3 \log_3 (x - 2) = -12$

9) $\log 6x = \log(x + 5)$

10) $\log(4p - 2) = \log(-5p + 5)$

11) $\log(4k - 5) = \log(2k - 1)$

12) $-10 + \log_3(n + 3) = -10$

13) $\log_9(x + 2) = \log_9(x^2 + 30)$

14) $\log_{12}(v^2 + 35) = \log_{12}(-2v - 1)$

15) $\log(16 + 2b) = \log(b^2 - 4b)$

16) $\log_9(x + 6) - \log_9(x) = \log_9 2$

17) $\log_5 6 + \log_5 2x^2 = \log_5 48$

18) $\log_6(x + 1) - \log_6 x = \log_6 29$

✎ *Find the value of x in each natural logarithm equation.*

19) $\ln 2 - \ln(3x + 2) = 1$

20) $\ln(x - 3) - \ln(x - 5) = \ln 5$

21) $\ln e^4 - \ln(x + 1) = 1$

22) $\ln(2x - 1) - \ln(x - 5) = \ln 5$

23) $\ln 2x + \ln(3x - 4) = \ln 4x$

24) $\ln(4x - 2) - 4 \ln(x - 5) = \ln 10$

25) $\ln(4x + 2) - \ln 1 = 5$

26) $\ln(x - 3) + \ln() \ln(x - 5) = \ln 2$

27) $\ln 2 + \ln(3x + 2) = 4$

28) $2 \ln 4x - \ln(x + 6) = 2 \ln 3x$

29) $\ln x^2 + \ln x^3 = \ln 1$

30) $\ln x^4 - \ln(x + 4) = 4 \ln x$

31) $2 \ln(x - 3) = \ln(x^2 - 6x + 9)$

32) $\ln(x^2 + 12) = \ln(6x + 4)$

33) $2 \ln x - 2 \ln(x + 2) = 4 \ln(x^2)$

34) $\ln(4x - 3) - \ln(2x - 4) = \ln 5$

35) $\ln 2 + 4 \ln(x + 2) = \ln 2$

36) $2 \ln e^2 + \ln(2x - 1) = \ln 5 + 4$

Answers – Chapter 9

Evaluating Logarithms

1) 2

2) 3

3) 3

4) 2

5) 2

6) 5

7) 2

8) -1

9) -3

10) -1

11) -2

12) -2

13) -2

14) $-\frac{1}{3}$

15) $\frac{1}{4}$

16) -6

17) -3

18) $-\frac{1}{2}$

19) $(2, 4)$

20) $(3, 4)$

21) $(3, -3)$

22) $(1, 11)$

23) $(-2, 1)$

24) $(4, 8)$

25) $(3, 6)$

Properties of Logarithms

1) $\log 8 + \log 5$

2) $\log 9 + \log 4$

3) $\log 3 + \log 7$

4) $\log 3 - \log 4$

5) $\log 5 - \log 7$

6) $3 \log 2 - 3 \log 5$

7) $\log 2 + 4 \log 3$

8) $4\log 5 - 4 \log 7$

9) $3 \log 2 - \log 7$

10) $5 \log x + 5 \log y$

11) $3 \log x + \log y + 4 \log z$

12) $4 \log u - \log v$

13) $\log x - 6 \log y$

14) $\log \frac{2}{9}$

15) $\log(5 \times 3)$

16) $\log \frac{6^5}{4^3}$

17) $\log \frac{7^4}{9^2}$

18) $\log \frac{5^3}{14}$

19) $\log \frac{3^7}{4^4}$

20) $\log \frac{7}{12^2}$

21) $\log (5^2 \times 8^3)$

22) $\log (3^4 \times 7^5)$

23) $\log_5 (a^4 \times b^7)$

24) $\log_3 \frac{x^2}{y^9}$

25) $\log_4 \frac{u}{v^6}$

26) $\log_6 (u^4 \times v^8)$

27) $\log_3 \frac{u^4}{v^{20}}$

Natural Logarithms

1) $x = \ln 3$
2) $x = \ln 4 , x = 2 \ln(2)$
3) $x = \ln 8 , x = 3 \ln(2)$
4) $x = e^6$
5) $x = e^{e^5}$
6) $x = \ln 9 , x = 2 \ln(3)$
7) $x = \dfrac{e^4 - 5}{2}$
8) $x = \dfrac{e+1}{2}$
9) $x = \dfrac{e+1}{6}$
10) $x = \sqrt{e}$
11) $x = \dfrac{e^{e^2}}{2}$
12) $x = 28$

13) $x = 80$
14) 0
15) 3
16) 2
17) 2
18) 4
19) -1
20) 10
21) 8
22) 32
23) $\dfrac{1}{2}$
24) $\dfrac{9}{25} = 0.36$
25) e

26) 6
27) -2
28) 16
29) $\dfrac{2}{e}$
30) 0
31) 3
32) -0.5
33) $4e^{-2} = \dfrac{4}{e^2}$
34) $\dfrac{1}{e}$
35) $3e$

Solving Logarithmic Equations

1) $\{2\}$
2) $\{\frac{1}{175}\}$
3) $\{\frac{1}{1,000}\}$
4) $\{4,000\}$
5) $\{5,000\}$
6) $\{1\}$
7) $\{6\}$
8) $\{83\}$
9) $\{1\}$
10) $\{\frac{7}{9}\}$
11) $\{2\}$
12) $\{\frac{7}{9}\}\{-2\}$

13) No Solution
14) No Solution
15) $\{8, -2\}$
16) $\{6\}$
17) $\{\sqrt{3}, -\sqrt{3}\}$
18) $\{\frac{1}{28}\}$
19) $x = \dfrac{2-2e}{3e} = -0.42$
20) $\{\frac{11}{2}\}$
21) $e^3 - 1$
22) $\{8\}$
23) $\{2\}$
24) $\{6.23\}$

25) $x = \dfrac{e^5 - 2}{4}$
26) $x = 4 + \sqrt{3}$
27) $x = \dfrac{e^4 - 4}{6}$
28) No Solution
29) $\{1\}$
30) No Solution
31) $x > 3$
32) $\{2, 4\}$
33) $\{0.71667 \dots\}$
34) $\{\frac{17}{6}\}$
35) $\{-1\}$
36) $\{3\}$

Chapter 10: Radical Expressions

Math Topics that you'll learn in this Chapter:

- ✓ Simplifying Radical Expressions
- ✓ Simplifying Radical Expressions Involving Fractions
- ✓ Multiplying Radical Expressions
- ✓ Adding and Subtracting Radical Expressions
- ✓ Domain and Range of Radical Functions
- ✓ Radical Equations

Chapter 10: Radical Expressions

Simplifying Radical Expressions

✎ **Simplify.**

1) $\sqrt{35x^2} =$

2) $\sqrt{90x^2} =$

3) $\sqrt[3]{8a} =$

4) $\sqrt{100x^3} =$

5) $\sqrt{125a} =$

6) $\sqrt[3]{88w^3} =$

7) $\sqrt{80x} =$

8) $\sqrt{216v} =$

9) $\sqrt[3]{125x}$

10) $\sqrt{64x^5} =$

11) $\sqrt{4x^2} =$

12) $\sqrt[3]{54a^2}$

13) $\sqrt{405} =$

14) $\sqrt{512p^3} =$

15) $\sqrt{216m^4} =$

16) $\sqrt{264x^3y^3} =$

17) $\sqrt{49x^3y^3} =$

18) $\sqrt{16a^4b^3} =$

19) $\sqrt{20x^3y^3} =$

20) $\sqrt[3]{216yx^3} =$

21) $3\sqrt{75x^2} =$

22) $5\sqrt{80x^2} =$

23) $\sqrt[3]{256x^2y^3} =$

24) $\sqrt[3]{343x^4y^2} =$

25) $4\sqrt{125a} =$

26) $\sqrt[3]{625xy} =$

27) $2\sqrt{8x^2y^3r} =$

28) $4\sqrt{36x^2y^3z^4} =$

29) $2\sqrt[3]{512x^3y^4} =$

30) $5\sqrt{64a^2b^3c^5} =$

Simplifying Radical Expressions Involving Fractions

✎ **Simplify.**

1) $\dfrac{\sqrt{5}}{\sqrt{3}} =$

2) $\dfrac{\sqrt{8}}{\sqrt{100}} =$

3) $\dfrac{\sqrt{2}}{2\sqrt{3}} =$

4) $\dfrac{4}{\sqrt{5}} =$

5) $\dfrac{2\sqrt{5r}}{\sqrt{m^3}} =$

6) $\dfrac{8\sqrt{3}}{\sqrt{k}} =$

7) $\dfrac{6\sqrt{14x^2}}{2\sqrt{18x}} =$

8) $\dfrac{\sqrt{7x^2y^2}}{\sqrt{5x^3v^2}} =$

9) $\dfrac{1}{1+\sqrt{2}} =$

10) $\dfrac{1-5\sqrt{a}}{\sqrt{11a}} =$

11) $\dfrac{\sqrt{a}}{\sqrt{a}+\sqrt{b}} =$

12) $\dfrac{1+\sqrt{2}}{3+\sqrt{5}} =$

13) $\dfrac{2+\sqrt{5}}{6-\sqrt{3}} =$

14) $\dfrac{5}{-3-3\sqrt{3}} =$

15) $\dfrac{2}{3+\sqrt{5}} =$

16) $\dfrac{\sqrt{7}-\sqrt{3}}{\sqrt{3}-\sqrt{7}} =$

17) $\dfrac{\sqrt{7}+\sqrt{5}}{\sqrt{5}+\sqrt{2}} =$

18) $\dfrac{3\sqrt{2}-\sqrt{7}}{4\sqrt{2}+\sqrt{5}} =$

19) $\dfrac{\sqrt{5}+2\sqrt{2}}{4-\sqrt{5}} =$

20) $\dfrac{5\sqrt{3}-3\sqrt{2}}{3\sqrt{2}-2\sqrt{3}} =$

21) $\dfrac{\sqrt{8a^5b^3}}{\sqrt{2ab^2}} =$

22) $\dfrac{6\sqrt{45x^3}}{3\sqrt{5x}} =$

Multiplying Radical Expressions

✍ *Simplify.*

1) $\sqrt{5} \times \sqrt{5} =$

2) $\sqrt{5} \times \sqrt{10} =$

3) $\sqrt{2} \times \sqrt{18} =$

4) $\sqrt{14} \times \sqrt{21} =$

5) $\sqrt{5} \times -4\sqrt{20} =$

6) $3\sqrt{12} \times \sqrt{6} =$

7) $5\sqrt{42} \times \sqrt{3} =$

8) $\sqrt{3} \times -\sqrt{25} =$

9) $\sqrt{99} \times \sqrt{48} =$

10) $5\sqrt{45} \times 3\sqrt{176} =$

11) $\sqrt{12}(3 + \sqrt{3}) =$

12) $\sqrt{23x^2} \times \sqrt{23x} =$

13) $-5\sqrt{12} \times -\sqrt{3} =$

14) $2\sqrt{20x^2} \times \sqrt{5x^2} =$

15) $\sqrt{12x^2} \times \sqrt{2x^3} =$

16) $-12\sqrt{7x} \times \sqrt{5x^3} =$

17) $-5\sqrt{9x^3} \times 6\sqrt{3x^2} =$

18) $-2\sqrt{12}(3 + \sqrt{12}) =$

19) $\sqrt{18x}(4 - \sqrt{6x}) =$

20) $\sqrt{3x}(6\sqrt{x^3} + \sqrt{27}) =$

21) $\sqrt{15r}(5 + \sqrt{5}) =$

22) $-5\sqrt{3x} \times 4\sqrt{6x^3} =$

23) $-2\sqrt{18x} \times 4\sqrt{2x}$

24) $-3\sqrt{5v^2}(-3\sqrt{15v}) =$

25) $(\sqrt{5} - \sqrt{3})(\sqrt{5} + \sqrt{3}) =$

26) $(-4\sqrt{6} + 2)(\sqrt{6} - 5) =$

27) $(2 - 2\sqrt{3})(-2 + \sqrt{3}) =$

28) $(11 - 4\sqrt{5})(6 - \sqrt{5}) =$

29) $(-2 - \sqrt{3x})(3 + \sqrt{3x}) =$

30) $(-2 + 3\sqrt{2r})(-2 + \sqrt{2r}) =$

31) $(-4\sqrt{2n} + 2)(-2\sqrt{2} - 4) =$

32) $(-1 + 2\sqrt{3})(2 - 3\sqrt{3x}) =$

Adding and Subtracting Radical Expressions

✎ *Simplify.*

1) $\sqrt{3} + \sqrt{27} =$

2) $3\sqrt{8} + 3\sqrt{2} =$

3) $4\sqrt{3} - 2\sqrt{12} =$

4) $3\sqrt{18} - 2\sqrt{2} =$

5) $2\sqrt{45} - 2\sqrt{5} =$

6) $-\sqrt{12} - 5\sqrt{3} =$

7) $-4\sqrt{2} - 5\sqrt{32} =$

8) $5\sqrt{10} + 2\sqrt{40} =$

9) $4\sqrt{12} - 3\sqrt{27} =$

10) $-3\sqrt{2} + 4\sqrt{18} =$

11) $-10\sqrt{7} + 6\sqrt{28} =$

12) $5\sqrt{3} - \sqrt{27} =$

13) $-\sqrt{12} + 3\sqrt{3} =$

14) $-3\sqrt{6} - \sqrt{54} =$

15) $3\sqrt{8} + 3\sqrt{2} =$

16) $2\sqrt{12} - 3\sqrt{27} =$

17) $\sqrt{50} - \sqrt{32} =$

18) $4\sqrt{8} - 6\sqrt{2} =$

19) $-4\sqrt{12} + 12\sqrt{108} =$

20) $2\sqrt{45} - 2\sqrt{5} =$

21) $7\sqrt{18} - 3\sqrt{2} =$

22) $-12\sqrt{35} + 7\sqrt{140} =$

23) $-6\sqrt{19} - 3\sqrt{76} =$

24) $-\sqrt{54x} - 3\sqrt{6x} =$

25) $\sqrt{5y^2} + y\sqrt{45} =$

26) $\sqrt{8mn^2} + 2n\sqrt{18m} =$

27) $-8\sqrt{27a} - 5\sqrt{3a} =$

28) $-4\sqrt{7ab} - \sqrt{28ab} =$

29) $\sqrt{27a^2b} + a\sqrt{12b} =$

30) $3\sqrt{6a^3} - 2\sqrt{24a^3} + 2a\sqrt{54a} =$

Domain and Range of Radical Functions

✍️ *Identify the domain and range of each function.*

1) $y = \sqrt{x + 2} - 3$

2) $y = \sqrt[3]{x - 1} - 1$

3) $y = \sqrt{x - 2} + 5$

4) $y = \sqrt[3]{(x + 1)} - 4$

5) $y = 3\sqrt{3x + 6} + 5$

6) $y = \sqrt[3]{(2x - 1)} - 4$

7) $y = 6\sqrt{3x^2 + 6} + 5$

8) $y = \sqrt[3]{(2x^2 - 2)} - 4$

9) $y = 4\sqrt{4x^3 + 32} - 1$

10) $y = \sqrt[3]{(4x + 8)} - 2x$

11) $y = 7\sqrt{-2(2x + 4)} + 1$

12) $y = \sqrt[5]{(4x^2 - 5)} - 2$

13) $y = 2x\sqrt{5x^4 + 6} - 2x$

14) $y = 6\sqrt[3]{(8x^6 + 2x + 8)} - 2$

✍️ *Sketch the graph of each function.*

15) $y = \sqrt{x} + 8$

16) $y = 2\sqrt{x} - 4$

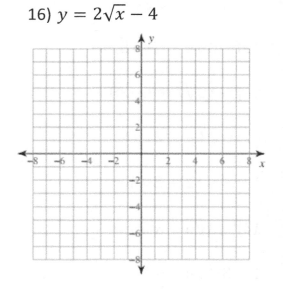

Chapter 10: Radical Expressions

Radical Equations

✏ *Solve each equation. Remember to check for extraneous solutions.*

1) $\sqrt{a} = 5$

2) $\sqrt{v} = 3$

3) $\sqrt{r} = 4$

4) $2 = 4\sqrt{x}$

5) $\sqrt{x+1} = 9$

6) $1 = \sqrt{x-5}$

7) $6 = \sqrt{r-2}$

8) $\sqrt{x-6} = 8$

9) $5 = \sqrt{x-3}$

10) $\sqrt{m+8} = 8$

11) $10\sqrt{9a} = 60$

12) $5\sqrt{3x} = 15$

13) $1 = \sqrt{3x-5}$

14) $\sqrt{12-x} = x$

15) $\sqrt{r+3} - 1 = 7$

16) $-12 = -6\sqrt{r+4}$

17) $20 = 2\sqrt{36v}$

18) $x = \sqrt{42-x}$

19) $\sqrt{110-a} = a$

20) $\sqrt{2n-12} = 2$

21) $\sqrt{3r-5} = r-3$

22) $\sqrt{-16+10x} = x$

23) $\sqrt{3x+12} = \sqrt{x+8}$

24) $\sqrt{v} = \sqrt{2v-6}$

25) $\sqrt{11-x} = \sqrt{x-7}$

26) $\sqrt{m+8} = \sqrt{3m+8}$

27) $\sqrt{2r+40} = \sqrt{-16-2r}$

28) $\sqrt{k+3} = \sqrt{1-k}$

29) $-10\sqrt{x-10} = -60$

30) $\sqrt{72-x} = \sqrt{\dfrac{x}{5}}$

Answers – Chapter 10

Simplifying Radical Expressions

1) $x\sqrt{35}$

2) $3x\sqrt{10}$

3) $2\sqrt[3]{a}$

4) $10x\sqrt{x}$

5) $5\sqrt{5a}$

6) $2w\sqrt[3]{11}$

7) $4\sqrt{5x}$

8) $6\sqrt{6v}$

9) $5\sqrt[3]{x}$

10) $8x^2\sqrt{x}$

11) $2x$

12) $3\sqrt[3]{2a^2}$

13) $9\sqrt{5}$

14) $16p\sqrt{2p}$

15) $6m^2\sqrt{6}$

16) $2x.\,y\sqrt{66xy}$

17) $7xy\sqrt{xy}$

18) $4a^2b\sqrt{b}$

19) $2xy\sqrt{5xy}$

20) $6x\sqrt[3]{y}$

21) $15x\sqrt{3}$

22) $20x\sqrt{5}$

23) $4y\sqrt[3]{4x^2}$

24) $7x\sqrt[3]{xy^2}$

25) $20\sqrt{5a}$

26) $5\sqrt[3]{5xy}$

27) $4xy\sqrt{2yr}$

28) $24xyz^2\sqrt{y}$

29) $16xy\sqrt[3]{y}$

30) $40abc^2\sqrt{bc}$

Simplifying Radical Expressions Involving Fractions

1) $\frac{\sqrt{15}}{3}$

2) $\frac{\sqrt{2}}{5}$

3) $\frac{\sqrt{6}}{6}$

4) $\frac{4\sqrt{5}}{5}$

5) $\frac{2\sqrt{5mr}}{m^2}$

6) $\frac{8\sqrt{3k}}{k}$

7) $\sqrt{7x}$

8) $\frac{y\sqrt{35x}}{5xv}$

9) $-1+\sqrt{2}$

10) $\frac{\sqrt{11a}-5a\sqrt{11}}{11a}$

11) $\frac{a-\sqrt{ab}}{a-b}$

12) $\frac{3-\sqrt{5}+3\sqrt{2}-\sqrt{10}}{4}$

13) $\frac{12+2\sqrt{3}+6\sqrt{5}+\sqrt{15}}{33}$

14) $-\frac{5(-1+\sqrt{3})}{6}$

15) $\frac{3-\sqrt{5}}{2}$

16) -1

17) $\frac{\sqrt{35}-\sqrt{14}+5-\sqrt{10}}{3}$

18) $\frac{24-3\sqrt{10}-4\sqrt{14}+\sqrt{35}}{27}$

19) $\frac{4\sqrt{5}+5+8\sqrt{2}+2\sqrt{10}}{11}$

20) $\frac{3\sqrt{6}+4}{2}$

21) $2a^2\sqrt{b}$

22) $6x$

Multiplying Radical Expressions

1) 5

2) $5\sqrt{2}$

3) 6

4) $7\sqrt{6}$

5) -40

6) $18\sqrt{2}$

7) $15\sqrt{14}$

8) $-5\sqrt{3}$

9) $12\sqrt{33}$

10) $180\sqrt{55}$

11) $6\sqrt{3} + 6$

12) $23x\sqrt{x}$

13) 30

14) $20x^2$

15) $2x^2\sqrt{6x}$

16) $-12x^2\sqrt{35}$

17) $-90x^2\sqrt{3x}$

18) $-12\sqrt{3} - 24$

19) $12\sqrt{2x} - 6x\sqrt{3}$

20) $6x^2\sqrt{3} + 9\sqrt{x}$

21) $5\sqrt{15r} + 5\sqrt{3r}$

22) $-60x^2\sqrt{2}$

23) $-48x$

24) $45v\sqrt{3v}$

25) 2

26) $22\sqrt{6} - 34$

27) $6\sqrt{3} - 10$

28) $86 - 35\sqrt{5}$

29) $-3x - 5\sqrt{3x} - 6$

30) $6r - 8\sqrt{2r} + 4$

31) $16\sqrt{n} + 16\sqrt{2n} - 4\sqrt{2} - 8$

32) $-2 + 3\sqrt{3x} + 4\sqrt{3} - 18\sqrt{x}$

Adding and Subtracting Radical Expressions

1) $4\sqrt{3}$

2) $9\sqrt{2}$

3) 0

4) $7\sqrt{2}$

5) $4\sqrt{5}$

6) $-7\sqrt{3}$

7) $-24\sqrt{2}$

8) $9\sqrt{10}$

9) $-\sqrt{3}$

10) $9\sqrt{2}$

11) $2\sqrt{7}$

12) $2\sqrt{3}$

13) $\sqrt{3}$

14) $-6\sqrt{6}$

15) $9\sqrt{2}$

16) $-5\sqrt{3}$

17) $\sqrt{2}$

18) $2\sqrt{2}$

19) $64\sqrt{3}$

20) $4\sqrt{5}$

21) $18\sqrt{2}$

22) $2\sqrt{35}$

23) $-12\sqrt{19}$

24) $-6\sqrt{6x}$

25) $4y\sqrt{5}$

26) $8n\sqrt{2m}$

27) $-29\sqrt{3a}$

28) $-6\sqrt{7ab}$

29) $5a\sqrt{3b}$

30) $5a\sqrt{6a}$

Domain and Range of Radical Functions

1) domain: $x \geq -2$
   range: $y \geq -3$

2) domain: {all real numbers}
   range: {all real numbers}

3) domain: $x \geq 2$
   range: $y \geq 5$

4) domain: {all real numbers}
   range: {all real numbers}

5) domain: $x \geq -2$
   range: $y \geq 5$

6) domain: {all real numbers}
   range: {all real numbers}

7) domain: {all real numbers}
   range: $y \geq 6\sqrt{6} + 5$

8) domain: {all real numbers}
   range: {all real numbers}

9) domain: $x \geq -2$
   range: $y \geq -1$

10) domain: {all real numbers}
    range: {all real numbers}

11) domain: $x \leq -2$
    range: $y \geq 1$

12) domain: {all real numbers}
    range: {all real numbers}

13) domain: {all real numbers}
    range: {all real numbers}

14) domain: {all real numbers}
    range: {all real numbers}

15)

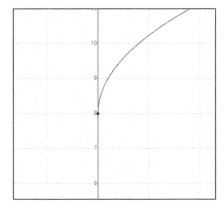

16)

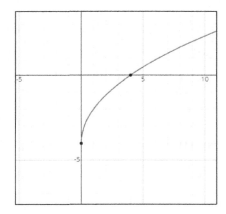

Radical Equations

1) $\{25\}$
2) $\{9\}$
3) $\{16\}$
4) $\{\frac{1}{4}\}$
5) $\{80\}$
6) $\{6\}$
7) $\{38\}$

8) $\{70\}$
9) $\{28\}$
10) $\{56\}$
11) $\{4\}$
12) $\{3\}$
13) $\{2\}$
14) $\{3\}$
15) $\{61\}$

16) $\{0\}$
17) $\{\frac{25}{9}\}$
18) $\{6\}$
19) $\{10\}$
20) $\{8\}$
21) $\{7\}$
22) $\{2, 8\}$

23) $\{-2\}$
24) $\{6\}$
25) $\{9\}$
26) $\{0\}$
27) $\{-14\}$
28) $\{-1\}$
29) $\{46\}$
30) $\{60\}$

Chapter 11: Rational and Irrational Expressions

Math Topics that you'll learn in this Chapter:

- ✓ Simplifying Rational Expressions
- ✓ Graphing Rational Expressions
- ✓ Multiplying Rational Expressions
- ✓ Dividing Rational Expressions
- ✓ Adding and Subtracting Rational Expressions
- ✓ Rational Equations
- ✓ Simplify Complex Fractions
- ✓ Maximum and Minimum Points

Simplifying Rational Expressions

✎ **Simplify.**

1) $\dfrac{6x^2}{4x} =$

2) $\dfrac{18x^4}{8x^2} =$

3) $\dfrac{16x^3}{20x^3} =$

4) $\dfrac{64x^3}{24x} =$

5) $\dfrac{25x^5}{15x^3} =$

6) $\dfrac{4}{2x-2} =$

7) $\dfrac{21}{3x-6} =$

8) $\dfrac{16}{2x-2} =$

9) $\dfrac{15x-3}{24} =$

10) $\dfrac{40}{10x-5} =$

11) $\dfrac{4x+16}{28} =$

12) $\dfrac{x^2-10x+25}{x-5} =$

13) $\dfrac{x^2-49}{x^2+3x-28} =$

14) $\dfrac{x^2+4x+4}{x^2-5x-14} =$

15) $\dfrac{x+3}{3x+9} =$

16) $\dfrac{2x^2-2x-12}{x-3} =$

17) $\dfrac{16}{4x-4} =$

18) $\dfrac{36x^3}{42x^3} =$

19) $\dfrac{x^2-3x-4}{x^2+2x-24} =$

20) $\dfrac{81x^3}{18x} =$

21) $\dfrac{x-3}{x^2-x-6} =$

22) $\dfrac{x^2-3x-28}{x-7} =$

23) $\dfrac{6x+18}{30} =$

24) $\dfrac{16}{4x-4} =$

Graphing Rational Expressions

✎ *Graph rational expressions.*

1) $f(x) = \dfrac{x^2 + x - 2}{x - 2}$

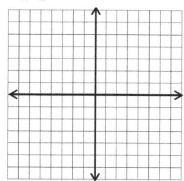

2) $f(x) = \dfrac{x^2 - 6x + 8}{2x - 4}$

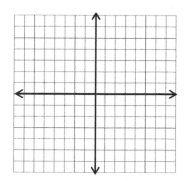

3) $f(x) = \dfrac{x^2 + 2x - 9}{x - 3}$

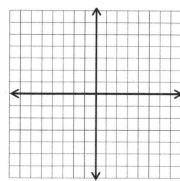

4) $f(x) = \dfrac{2x^3 - 15x + 45}{x^2 - 2x - 4}$

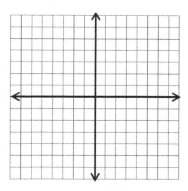

5) $f(x) = \dfrac{x^3 - 8x}{2x - 3}$

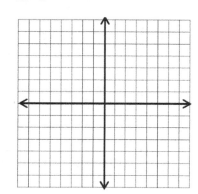

6) $f(x) = \dfrac{x^4 + x^2 + 2x}{x^2 + 4x}$

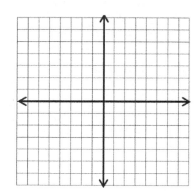

Chapter 11: Rational and Irrational Expressions

Multiplying Rational Expressions

✎ *Simplify each expression.*

1) $\dfrac{84}{3} \times \dfrac{48x}{95} =$

2) $\dfrac{53}{43} \times \dfrac{46x^2}{31} =$

3) $\dfrac{79x}{25} \times \dfrac{85}{27x^2} =$

4) $\dfrac{96x^3}{7x} \times \dfrac{119}{68x} =$

5) $\dfrac{96}{38x} \times \dfrac{25}{45} =$

6) $\dfrac{93}{21x} \times \dfrac{34x}{51x} =$

7) $\dfrac{85}{16x} \times \dfrac{48x}{95} =$

8) $\dfrac{2}{43x} \times \dfrac{46x^5}{38x} =$

9) $\dfrac{27x}{81} \times \dfrac{14x}{51x^2} =$

10) $\dfrac{5x+50}{x+10} \times \dfrac{x-2}{5} =$

11) $\dfrac{x-7}{x+6} \times \dfrac{10x+60}{x-7} =$

12) $\dfrac{1}{x+10} \times \dfrac{10x+30}{x+3} =$

13) $\dfrac{12x}{14} \times \dfrac{14}{16x} =$

14) $\dfrac{79x}{25} \times \dfrac{85}{27x^2} =$

15) $\dfrac{8(x+1)}{7x} \times \dfrac{9}{8(x+1)} =$

16) $\dfrac{2(x+6)}{4} \times \dfrac{x-3}{2(x-1)} =$

17) $\dfrac{9(x+4)}{x+4} \times \dfrac{9x}{9(x-5)} =$

18) $\dfrac{4x+20}{x+5} \times \dfrac{x-2}{4} =$

19) $\dfrac{x-3}{x+4} \times \dfrac{5x+30}{x-5} =$

20) $\dfrac{1}{x+4} \times \dfrac{4x+20}{x+5} =$

21) $\dfrac{3x^2+18x}{x+6} \times \dfrac{1}{x+8} =$

22) $\dfrac{21x^2-21x}{18x^2-18x} \times \dfrac{6x}{6x^2} =$

23) $\dfrac{1}{x-9} \times \dfrac{x^2+6x-27}{x+9} =$

24) $\dfrac{x^2-10x+25}{10x-100} \times \dfrac{x-10}{45-9x} =$

Dividing Rational Expressions

✍ *Divide.*

1) $\dfrac{12x}{3} \div \dfrac{5}{8} =$

2) $\dfrac{10x^2}{7} \div \dfrac{3x}{12} =$

3) $\dfrac{12x}{3} \div \dfrac{5}{8} =$

4) $\dfrac{9x}{x+5} \div \dfrac{9x}{2x+10} =$

5) $\dfrac{x^2}{9} \div \dfrac{3}{18x} =$

6) $\dfrac{11x}{x-7} \div \dfrac{11x}{12x-84} =$

7) $\dfrac{x+5}{5x^2-10x} \div \dfrac{1}{5x} =$

8) $\dfrac{x-2}{7x-12} \div \dfrac{x}{x+3} =$

9) $\dfrac{5x}{x-10} \div \dfrac{5x}{x-5} =$

10) $\dfrac{1}{2x} \div \dfrac{8x}{2x^2+16x} =$

11) $\dfrac{x^2+10x+16}{x^2+6x+8} \div \dfrac{1}{x+4} =$

12) $\dfrac{x^2-2x-15}{8x+20} \div \dfrac{2}{4x+10} =$

13) $\dfrac{x-4}{x^2-2x-8} \div \dfrac{1}{x-5} =$

14) $\dfrac{8+2x-x^2}{x^2-2x-8} \div \dfrac{4x}{x+6} =$

15) $\dfrac{x+10}{9x^2-90x} \div \dfrac{1}{9x} =$

16) $\dfrac{x-2}{x+6x-16} \div \dfrac{11x}{x+9} =$

17) $\dfrac{x^2-x-12}{8x+2} \div \dfrac{4}{4x+1} =$

18) $\dfrac{x-7}{-x^2+10x-21} \div \dfrac{1}{x-3} =$

19) $\dfrac{3x}{x-5} \div \dfrac{3x}{10x-50} =$

20) $\dfrac{x+5}{x+13x+40} \div \dfrac{4x}{x+9} =$

21) $\dfrac{x+4}{x+14x+40} \div \dfrac{6x}{x+9} =$

22) $\dfrac{14x+12}{3} \div \dfrac{63x+54}{3x} =$

23) $\dfrac{7x^3+49x^2}{x^2+12x+35} \div \dfrac{2}{2x^3-12x^2} =$

24) $\dfrac{x^2+10x+16}{x^2+6x+8} \div \dfrac{1}{x+8} =$

Chapter 11: Rational and Irrational Expressions

Adding and Subtracting Rational Expressions

✑ *Simplify each expression.*

1) $\dfrac{2}{x+3} + \dfrac{3}{x-2} =$

2) $\dfrac{3}{x+7} - \dfrac{4}{x-8} =$

3) $\dfrac{4}{x+1} - \dfrac{2}{x+2} =$

4) $\dfrac{2x}{5x+4} + \dfrac{6x}{2x+3} =$

5) $\dfrac{4x}{x+2} + \dfrac{x-3}{x+1} =$

6) $\dfrac{x}{x+1} + \dfrac{x+1}{x+2} =$

7) $\dfrac{x}{3x+2} + \dfrac{3x}{2x+3} =$

8) $\dfrac{4}{x+1} - \dfrac{2}{x+2} =$

9) $\dfrac{2}{3x^2+12x} + \dfrac{8}{2x} =$

10) $\dfrac{x}{10x+5} + \dfrac{5x}{2x+1} =$

11) $\dfrac{2}{6x+10} + \dfrac{x-6}{6x+10} =$

12) $\dfrac{x+5}{4x^2+20x} - \dfrac{x-5}{4x^2+20x} =$

13) $\dfrac{2}{x^2-5x+4} + \dfrac{2}{x^2-4} =$

14) $\dfrac{x-5}{x^2-6} - \dfrac{x-1}{6-x^2} =$

15) $\dfrac{4}{6x+8} + \dfrac{x-8}{6x+8} =$

16) $\dfrac{x+2}{x-4} + \dfrac{x-2}{x+3} =$

17) $\dfrac{x-7}{x^2-16} - \dfrac{x-1}{16-x^2} =$

18) $\dfrac{5}{x+5} + \dfrac{4x}{2x+6} =$

19) $2 + \dfrac{x-3}{x+1} =$

20) $\dfrac{3x-1}{5x+4} + \dfrac{x+3}{2x+6} =$

21) $\dfrac{5xy}{x^2-y^2} - \dfrac{x-y}{x+y} =$

22) $\dfrac{5x+5}{5x^2+35x-40} + \dfrac{7x}{3x} =$

23) $3 + \dfrac{x}{x+2} - \dfrac{2}{x^2-4} =$

24) $\dfrac{x+2}{3x^2+10x} + \dfrac{x-2}{3x^2+10x} =$

Rational Equations

✍ *Solve each equation. Remember to check for extraneous solutions.*

1) $\dfrac{x-1}{x+3} = \dfrac{4}{x-3}$

2) $\dfrac{3}{x-2} = \dfrac{2x}{x-2}$

3) $\dfrac{4}{b-7} = \dfrac{-2b}{b+3}$

4) $\dfrac{9}{n+1} = \dfrac{n}{n-1}$

5) $\dfrac{x}{4} = \dfrac{x+2}{6}$

6) $\dfrac{2-x}{1-x} = \dfrac{12}{4-x}$

7) $\dfrac{2}{x^2-x} = \dfrac{1}{x-1}$

8) $\dfrac{5x}{2x^2-4} = \dfrac{10}{x-5}$

9) $\dfrac{2x-3}{x+1} = \dfrac{x+6}{x-2}$

10) $\dfrac{1}{x} = \dfrac{6}{5x} + 1$

11) $\dfrac{x+6}{x+3} = \dfrac{x+6}{x+1}$

12) $\dfrac{1}{6b^2} + \dfrac{1}{6b} = \dfrac{1}{b^2}$

13) $\dfrac{3x-2}{9x+1} = \dfrac{2x-5}{6x-5}$

14) $\dfrac{1}{n^2} + \dfrac{1}{n} = \dfrac{1}{2n^2}$

15) $\dfrac{1}{8b^2} = \dfrac{1}{4b^2} - \dfrac{1}{b}$

16) $\dfrac{1}{n-8} - 1 = \dfrac{7}{n-8}$

17) $\dfrac{5}{r-2} = -\dfrac{10}{r+2} + 7$

18) $1 = \dfrac{1}{x^2+2x} + \dfrac{x-1}{x}$

19) $\dfrac{1}{x} = 8 + \dfrac{6}{9x}$

20) $\dfrac{x+5}{x^2-2x} - 1 = \dfrac{1}{x^2-2x}$

21) $\dfrac{x-2}{x+3} - 1 = \dfrac{1}{x+2}$

22) $\dfrac{1}{6x^2} = \dfrac{1}{3x^2} - \dfrac{1}{x}$

23) $\dfrac{x+5}{x^2-x} = \dfrac{1}{x^2+x} - \dfrac{x-6}{x+1}$

24) $1 = \dfrac{1}{x^2-2x} + \dfrac{x-1}{x}$

Chapter 11: Rational and Irrational Expressions

Simplify Complex Fractions

✎ *Simplify each expression.*

1) $\dfrac{\frac{12}{3}}{\frac{2}{15}} =$

2) $\dfrac{\frac{14}{3}}{-6\frac{2}{11}} =$

3) $\dfrac{-1\frac{11}{12}}{-3} =$

4) $\dfrac{\frac{4}{5}}{\frac{2}{25}-\frac{5}{16}} =$

5) $\dfrac{8}{\frac{8}{x}+\frac{2}{3x}} =$

6) $\dfrac{x}{\frac{2}{5}-\frac{2}{x}} =$

7) $\dfrac{\frac{2}{x+2}}{\frac{8}{x^2+6x+8}} =$

8) $\dfrac{\frac{12}{x-1}}{\frac{12}{5}-\frac{12}{25}} =$

9) $\dfrac{1+\frac{2}{x-4}}{1-\frac{6}{x-4}} =$

10) $\dfrac{\frac{x+6}{4}}{\frac{x^2}{2}-\frac{5}{2}} =$

11) $\dfrac{\frac{x-2}{x-6}}{\frac{8}{x-2}+\frac{2}{9}} =$

12) $\dfrac{9}{\frac{9}{x}+\frac{2}{3x}} =$

13) $\dfrac{x^2}{\frac{4}{5}-\frac{4}{x}} =$

14) $\dfrac{\frac{4}{x-3}-\frac{2}{x+2}}{\frac{8}{x^2+6x+8}} =$

15) $\dfrac{\frac{16}{x-1}}{\frac{16}{5}-\frac{16}{25}} =$

16) $\dfrac{2+\frac{6}{x-4}}{2-\frac{4}{x-4}} =$

17) $\dfrac{\frac{1}{2}-\frac{x+5}{4}}{\frac{x^2}{2}-\frac{5}{2}} =$

18) $\dfrac{\frac{x-6}{2}-\frac{x-2}{x-6}}{\frac{36}{x-2}+\frac{4}{9}} =$

Maximum and Minimum Points

✎ *Find the maximum and minimum points of the function.*

1) $f(x) = 2x^2 - 4x + 6$

Maximum: _____

Minimum: _____

2) $f(x) = x^3 + 4x + 1$

Maximum: _____

Minimum: _____

3) $f(x) = x^3 - 3x + 2$

Maximum: _____

Minimum: _____

4) $f(x) = 3x^2 + 4x + 3$

Maximum: _____

Minimum: _____

5) $f(x) = 4x^2 - 3$

Maximum: _____

Minimum: _____

6) $f(x) = x^3 + x^2 - 8x - 6$

Maximum: _____

Minimum: _____

7) $f(x) = \frac{4}{x^2 + 2}$

Maximum: _____

Minimum: _____

8) $f(x) = x^3 + 2x$

Maximum: _____

Minimum: _____

9) $f(x) = -x^3 - 6x^2 - 9x + 2$

Maximum: _____

Minimum: _____

10) $f(x) = 4x^2 - 16x + 3$

Maximum: _____

Minimum: _____

11) $f(x) = 9x + \frac{1}{x}$

Maximum: _____

Minimum: _____

12) $f(x) = \frac{x}{(1+x)^2}$

Maximum: _____

Minimum: _____

13) $f(x) = 3x^4 - 8x^3 + 6$

Maximum: _____

Minimum: _____

14) $f(x) = -2x^3 - 4x^2 + 2$

Maximum: _____

Minimum: _____

Answers – Chapter 11

Simplifying Rational Expressions

1) $\frac{3x}{2}$

2) $\frac{9x^2}{4}$

3) $\frac{4}{5}$

4) $\frac{8x^2}{3}$

5) $\frac{5x^2}{3}$

6) $\frac{2}{x-1}$

7) $\frac{7}{x-2}$

8) $\frac{8}{x-1}$

9) $\frac{5x-1}{8}$

10) $\frac{8}{2x-1}$

11) $\frac{x+4}{7}$

12) $x-5$

13) $\frac{x-7}{x-4}$

14) $\frac{x+2}{x-7}$

15) $\frac{1}{3}$

16) $2x+4$

17) $\frac{4}{x-1}$

18) $\frac{6}{7}$

19) $\frac{x+1}{x+6}$

20) $\frac{9x^2}{2}$

21) $\frac{1}{x+2}$

22) $x+4$

23) $\frac{x+3}{5}$

24) $\frac{4}{x-1}$

Graphing Rational Expressions

1) $f(x) = \frac{x^2+x-2}{x-2}$

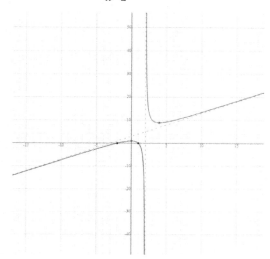

2) $f(x) = \frac{x^2-6x+8}{2x-4}$

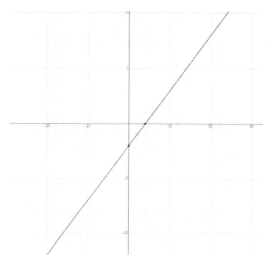

3) $f(x) = \frac{x^2+2x-9}{x-3}$

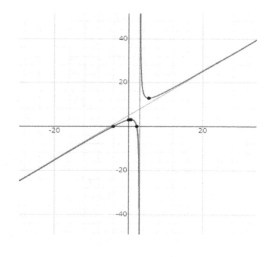

4) $f(x) = \frac{2x^3-15x+45}{x^2-2x-4}$

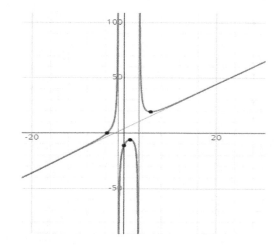

5) $f(x) = \frac{x^3 - 8x}{2x - 3}$

6) $f(x) = \frac{x^4 + x^2 + 2x}{x^2 + 4x}$

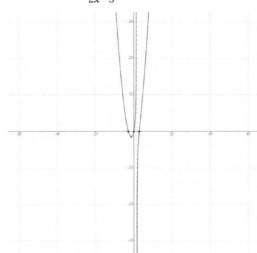

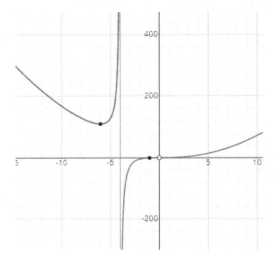

Multiplying Rational Expressions

1) $\frac{1,344x}{95}$

2) $\frac{2,438x^2}{1,333}$

3) $\frac{1,343}{135x}$

4) $24x$

5) $\frac{80}{57x}$

6) $\frac{62}{21x}$

7) $\frac{51}{19}$

8) $\frac{46x^3}{817}$

9) $\frac{14}{153}$

10) $x - 2$

11) 10

12) $\frac{10}{x + 10}$

13) $\frac{3}{4}$

14) $\frac{1,343}{135x}$

15) $\frac{9}{7x}$

16) $\frac{(x+6)(x-3)}{4(x-1)}$

17) $\frac{9x}{x - 5}$

18) $x - 2$

19) $\frac{(x-3)(5x+30)}{(x+4)(x-5)}$

20) $\frac{4}{x + 4}$

21) $\frac{3x}{x + 8}$

22) $\frac{7}{6x}$

23) $\frac{x-3}{x-9}$

24) $-\frac{(x-5)}{90}$

Dividing Rational Expressions

1) $\frac{32}{5}x$

2) $\frac{40x}{7}$

3) $\frac{32}{5}x$

4) 2

5) $\frac{2x^3}{3}$

6) 12

7) $\frac{x+5}{x-2}$

8) $\frac{(x-2)(x+3)}{x(7x-12)}$

9) $\frac{(x-5)}{(x-10)}$

10) $\frac{x+8}{8x}$

11) $x+8$

12) $\frac{(x+3)(x-5)}{4}$

13) $\frac{x-5}{x+2}$

14) $-\frac{x+6}{4x}$

15) $\frac{x+10}{x-10}$

16) $\frac{(x+9)(x-2)}{11x(7x-16)}$

17) $\frac{(x+3)(x-4)}{8}$

18) -1

19) 10

20) $\frac{(x+5)(x+9)}{4x(14x+40)}$

21) $\frac{(x+9)(x+4)}{6x(15x+40)}$

22) $\frac{2x}{9}$

23) $\frac{7x^4(x-6)}{x+5}$

24) $\frac{(x+8)^2}{x+4}$

Adding and Subtracting Rational Expressions

1) $\frac{5x+5}{(x+3)(x-2)}$

2) $\frac{-x-52}{(x+7)(x-8)}$

3) $\frac{2x+6}{(x+1)(x+2)}$

4) $\frac{34x^2+30x}{(5x+4)(2x+3)}$

5) $\frac{5x^2+3x-6}{(x+2)(x+1)}$

6) $\frac{2x^2+4x+1}{(x+1)(x+2)}$

7) $\frac{11x^2+9x}{(3x+2)(2x+3)}$

8) $\frac{2x+6}{(x+1)(x+2)}$

9) $\frac{50+12x}{3x(x+4)}$

10) $\frac{26x}{5(2x+1)}$

11) $\frac{-4+x}{6x+10}$

12) $\frac{5}{2x(x+5)}$

13) $\frac{4x^2-10x}{(x-1)(x-4)(x+2)(x-2)}$

14) $\frac{2x-6}{x^2-6}$

15) $\frac{-4+x}{6x+8}$

16) $\frac{2x^2-x+14}{(x-4)(x+3)}$

17) $\frac{2}{x+4}$

18) $\frac{2x^2+15x+15}{(x+5)(x+3)}$

19) $\frac{3x-1}{x+1}$

20) $\frac{11x+2}{2(5x+4)}$

21) $\frac{-x^3+6xy^2-y^3+6x^2y}{(x^2-y^2)(x+y)}$

22) $\frac{52x-53+7x^2}{3(x+8)(x-1)}$

23) $\frac{4x^2-2x-14}{(x+2)(x-2)}$

24) $\frac{2}{3x+10}$

Rational Equations

1) $\{9, -1\}$

2) $\{\frac{3}{2}\}$

3) $\{2, 3\}$

4) $\{4 + \sqrt{7}, 4 - \sqrt{7}\}$

5) $\{4\}$

6) $\{-3 + \sqrt{13}, -3 - \sqrt{13}\}$

7) $\{2\}$

8) $\{-\frac{8}{3}, 1\}$

9) $\{14, 0\}$

10) $\{-\frac{1}{5}\}$

11) $\{-6\}$

12) $\{5\}$

13) $\{-\frac{15}{16}\}$

14) $\{-\frac{1}{2}\}$

15) $\{\frac{1}{8}\}$

16) $\{2\}$

17) $\{-\frac{6}{7}, 3\}$

18) $\{-1\}$

19) $\{\frac{1}{24}\}$

20) $\{4, -1\}$

21) $\{-\frac{13}{6}\}$

22) $\{\frac{1}{6}\}$

23) $\{-0.43484\}$

24) $\{3\}$

Simplify Complex Fractions

1) 30

2) $-\frac{77}{102}$

3) $\frac{23}{36}$

4) $-\frac{320}{93}$

5) $\frac{12x}{13}$

6) $\frac{5x^2}{2x-10}$

7) $\frac{(x+4)}{4}$

8) $\frac{25}{4(x-1)}$

9) $\frac{x-2}{x-10}$

10) $\frac{x+6}{2x^2-10}$

11) $\frac{9(x-2)^2}{(2x+68)(x-6)}$

12) $\frac{27x}{29}$

13) $\frac{5x^3}{4x-20}$

14) $\frac{(x+7)(x+4)}{4(x-3)}$

15) $\frac{25}{4x-4}$

16) $\frac{x-1}{x-6}$

17) $\frac{-3-x}{2x^2-10}$

18) $\frac{9x^3-144x^2+612x-720}{584x+8x^2-3,792}$

Maximum and Minimum Points

1) Minimum: $(1,4)$

2) Maximum: *none*
   Minimum: *none*

3) Maximum: $(-1,4)$
   Minimum: $(1,0)$

4) Minimum: $(-\frac{2}{3},\frac{5}{3})$

5) Minimum: $(0,-3)$

6) Maximum: $(-2,6)$
   Minimum: $(\frac{4}{3},-\frac{338}{27})$

7) Maximum: $(0,2)$

8) Maximum: *none*

Minimum: *none*

9) Maximum: $(-1,6)$
   Minimum: $(-3,2)$

10) Minimum: $(2,-13)$

11) Maximum: $(-\frac{1}{3},-6)$
    Minimum: $(\frac{1}{3},6)$

12) Maximum: $(1,\frac{1}{4})$

13) Minimum: $(2,-10)$

14) Maximum: $(0,2)$
    Minimum: $(-\frac{4}{3},-\frac{10}{27})$

Chapter 12:
Trigonometric Functions

Math Topics that you'll learn in this Chapter:

- ✓ Trig Ratios of General Angles
- ✓ Coterminal Angles and Reference Angles
- ✓ Angles and Angle Measure
- ✓ Evaluating Trigonometric Function
- ✓ Missing Sides and Angles of a Right Triangle
- ✓ Arc length and Sector Area

127

Trig Ratios of General Angles

✏ *Evaluate.*

1) $sin -60° = $ _____

2) $sin 150° = $ _____

3) $cos 315° = $ _____

4) $cos 180° = $ _____

5) $sin 120° = $ _____

6) $sin -330° = $ _____

7) $tan -90° = $ _____

8) $cot 90° = $ _____

9) $tan 270° = $ _____

10) $cot 150° = $ _____

11) $sec 120° = $ _____

12) $csc -360° = $ _____

13) $cot -270° = $ _____

14) $sec 90° = $ _____

15) $cos -90° = $ _____

16) $sec 60° = $ _____

17) $csc 480° = $ _____

18) $cot -135° = $ _____

✏ *Find the exact value of each trigonometric function. Some may be undefined.*

19) $sec \pi = $ _____

20) $tan -\dfrac{3\pi}{2} = $ _____

21) $cos \dfrac{11\pi}{6} = $ _____

22) $cot \dfrac{5\pi}{3} = $ _____

23) $sec -\dfrac{3\pi}{4} = $ _____

24) $sec \dfrac{\pi}{3} = $ _____

25) $csc \dfrac{5\pi}{6} = $ _____

26) $cot \dfrac{4\pi}{3} = $ _____

27) $csc -\dfrac{3\pi}{4} = $ _____

28) $cot \dfrac{2\pi}{3} = $ _____

Coterminal Angles and Reference Angles

✎ *Find a positive and a negative coterminal angle for each given angle.*

1) $75° =$

2) $115° =$

3) $85° =$

4) $170° =$

5) $220° =$

6) $95° =$

7) $120° =$

8) $55° =$

9) $135° =$

10) $140° =$

11) $185° =$

12) $235° =$

13) $95° =$

14) $165° =$

15) $\dfrac{\pi}{3} =$

16) $\dfrac{\pi}{4} =$

17) $\dfrac{5\pi}{4} =$

18) $\dfrac{2\pi}{5} =$

19) $-\dfrac{5\pi}{6} =$

20) $-\dfrac{\pi}{12} =$

21) $\dfrac{7\pi}{9} =$

22) $\dfrac{3\pi}{4} =$

Angles and Angle Measure

✎ **Convert each degree measure to a radian measure.**

1) $45° =$

2) $90° =$

3) $30° =$

4) $70° =$

5) $50° =$

6) $85° =$

7) $120° =$

8) $110° =$

9) $130° =$

10) $250° =$

11) $210° =$

12) $600° =$

✎ **Convert each radian measure to a degree measure.**

13) $\frac{\pi}{4} =$

14) $\frac{\pi}{5} =$

15) $\frac{\pi}{6} =$

16) $\frac{\pi}{3} =$

17) $\frac{3\pi}{4} =$

18) $\frac{5\pi}{6} =$

19) $-\frac{3\pi}{2} =$

20) $-\frac{7\pi}{3} =$

21) $\frac{11\pi}{5} =$

22) $\frac{15\pi}{12} =$

23) $-\frac{14\pi}{5} =$

24) $\frac{25\pi}{12} =$

Evaluating Trigonometric Function

✍ *Find the exact value of each trigonometric function.*

1) $\cos 120° =$

2) $\sin -\dfrac{\pi}{4} =$

3) $\cos 135° =$

4) $\sec 150° =$

5) $\sin 225° =$

6) $\cot -45° =$

7) $\csc 60° =$

8) $\tan -\dfrac{\pi}{3} =$

9) $\cos \dfrac{5\pi}{3} =$

10) $\sec 120° =$

11) $\cos 240° =$

12) $\sin -\dfrac{11\pi}{6} =$

13) $\cos 255° =$

14) $\sec -\dfrac{7\pi}{6} =$

15) $\cos \dfrac{13\pi}{5} =$

16) $\cot 120° =$

17) $\csc -\dfrac{\pi}{6} =$

18) $\tan 225° =$

19) $\cos -\dfrac{3\pi}{2} =$

20) $\sec 345° =$

21) $\tan -\dfrac{13\pi}{8} =$

22) $\cot 240° =$

Missing Sides and Angles of a Right Triangle

✎ *Find the missing sides. Round answers to the nearest tenth.*

1) _____

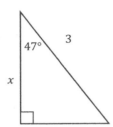

2) _____

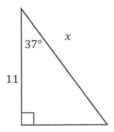

3) _____

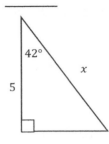

4) _____

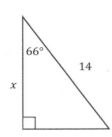

5) _____

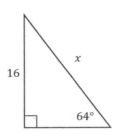

6) _____

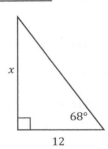

7) _____

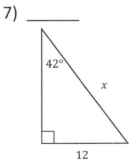

8) _____

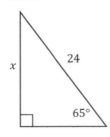

9) _____

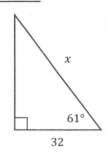

Arc Length and Sector Area

✎ *Find the length of each arc. Round your answers to the nearest tenth.*

($\pi = 3.14$)

1) $r = 28\ cm,\ \theta = 45^{\circ}$ 3) $r = 22\ ft,\ \theta = 60^{\circ}$

2) $r = 15\ ft,\ \theta = 95^{\circ}$ 4) $r = 12\ m,\ \theta = 85^{\circ}$

✎ *Find the area of each sector. Round your answers to the nearest tenth.*

($\pi = 3.14$)

5) _____

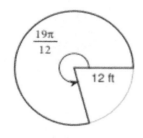

6) _____

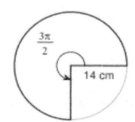

7) _____

8) _____

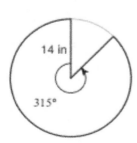

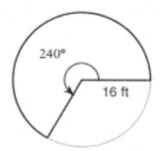

Trig Ratios of General Angles

1) $-\frac{\sqrt{3}}{2}$

2) $\frac{1}{2}$

3) $\frac{\sqrt{2}}{2}$

4) -1

5) $\frac{\sqrt{3}}{2}$

6) $\frac{1}{2}$

7) Undefined

8) 0

9) Undefined

10) $-\sqrt{3}$

11) -2

12) Undefined

13) 0

14) Undefined

15) 0

16) 2

17) $\frac{2\sqrt{3}}{3}$

18) 1

19) -1

20) Undefined

21) $\frac{\sqrt{3}}{2}$

22) $-\frac{\sqrt{3}}{3}$

23) $-\sqrt{2}$

24) 2

25) 2

26) $\frac{\sqrt{3}}{3}$

27) $-\sqrt{2}$

28) $-\frac{\sqrt{3}}{3}$

Coterminal Angles and Reference Angles

1) $-285°$ and a $435°$

2) $-245°$ and a $475°$

3) $-275°$ and a $445°$

4) $-190°$ and a $530°$

5) $-140°$ and a $580°$

6) $-265°$ and a $455°$

7) $-240°$ and a $480°$

8) $-305°$ and a $415°$

9) $-225°$ and a $495°$

10) $-220°$ and a $500°$

11) $-175°$ and a $545°$

12) $-125°$ and a $595°$

13) $-265°$ and a $455°$

14) $-195°$ and a $525°$

15) $-\frac{5\pi}{3}$ and a $\frac{7\pi}{3}$

16) $-\frac{7\pi}{4}$ and a $\frac{9\pi}{4}$

17) $-\frac{3\pi}{4}$ and a $\frac{13\pi}{4}$

18) $-\frac{8\pi}{5}$ and a $\frac{12\pi}{5}$

19) $-\frac{17\pi}{6}$ and a $\frac{7\pi}{6}$

20) $-\frac{25\pi}{12}$ and a $\frac{23\pi}{12}$

21) $-\frac{11\pi}{9}$ and a $\frac{25\pi}{9}$

22) $-\frac{5\pi}{4}$ and a $\frac{11\pi}{4}$

Angles and Angle Measure

1) $\frac{\pi}{4}$

2) $\frac{\pi}{2}$

3) $\frac{\pi}{6}$

4) $\frac{7\pi}{18}$

5) $\frac{5\pi}{18}$

6) $\frac{17\pi}{36}$

7) $\frac{2\pi}{3}$

8) $\frac{11\pi}{18}$

9) $\frac{13\pi}{18}$

10) $\frac{25\pi}{18}$

11) $\frac{7\pi}{6}$

12) $\frac{10\pi}{3}$

13) $45°$

14) $36°$

15) $30°$

16) $60°$

17) $135°$

18) $150°$

19) $-270°$

20) $-420°$

21) $396°$

22) $225°$

23) $-504°$

24) $375°$

Evaluating Trigonometric Function

1) $-\frac{1}{2}$

2) $-\frac{\sqrt{2}}{2}$

3) $-\frac{\sqrt{2}}{2}$

4) $-\frac{2\sqrt{3}}{3}$

5) $-\frac{\sqrt{2}}{2}$

6) -1

7) $\frac{2\sqrt{3}}{3}$

8) $-\sqrt{3}$

9) $\frac{1}{2}$

10) -2

11) $-\frac{1}{2}$

12) $\frac{1}{2}$

13) $\frac{\sqrt{2}-\sqrt{6}}{4}$

14) $-\frac{2\sqrt{3}}{3}$

15) $-\frac{\sqrt{2}\sqrt{3}-\sqrt{5}}{4}$

16) $-\frac{\sqrt{3}}{3}$

17) -2

18) 1

19) 0

20) $-\sqrt{2}+\sqrt{6}$

21) $\sqrt{2}+1$

22) $\frac{\sqrt{3}}{3}$

Missing Sides and Angles of a Right Triangle

1) 2
2) 13.8
3) 6.7
4) 5.7
5) 17.8
6) 29.7
7) 17.9
8) 21.8
9) 66

Arc Length and Sector Area

1) 22 cm
2) 24.9 ft
3) 23 ft
4) 17.8 m
5) 358 ft^2
6) 461.6 cm^2
7) 538.5 in^2
8) 535.9 ft^2

Chapter 13:
Sequences and Series

Math Topics that you'll learn in this Chapter:

- ✓ Arithmetic Sequences
- ✓ Geometric Sequences
- ✓ Arithmetic Series
- ✓ Finite Geometric Series
- ✓ Infinite Geometric Series
- ✓ Pascal's Triangle
- ✓ Binomial Theorem
- ✓ Sigma Notation (Summation Notation)

137

Arithmetic Sequences

✍ **Find the next three terms of each arithmetic sequence.**

1) $15, 11, 7, 3, -1, \ldots$

2) $-21, -14, -7, 0, \ldots$

3) $3, 6, 9, 12, 15, \ldots$

4) $4, 8, 12, 16, 20, \ldots$

✍ **Given the first term and the common difference of an arithmetic sequence find the first five terms and the explicit formula.**

5) $a_1 = 24, d = 2$

6) $a_1 = -15, d = -5$

7) $a_1 = 18, d = 10$

8) $a_1 = -38, d = -100$

✍ **Given a term in an arithmetic sequence and the common difference find the first five terms and the explicit formula.**

9) $a_{36} = -276, d = -7$

10) $a_{37} = 249, d = 8$

11) $a_{38} = -53.2, d = -1.1$

12) $a_{40} = -1,191, d = -30$

✍ **Given a term in an arithmetic sequence and the common difference find the recursive formula and the three terms in the sequence after the last one given.**

13) $a_{22} = -44, d = -2$

14) $a_{12} = 28.6, d = 1.8$

15) $a_{18} = 27.4, d = 1.1$

16) $a_{21} = -1.4, d = 0.6$

Geometric Sequences

✎ *Determine if the sequence is geometric. If it is, find the common ratio.*

1) $1, -5, 25, -125, \dots$

3) $4, 16, 36, 64, \dots$

2) $-2, -4, -8, -16, \dots$

4) $-3, -15, -75, -375, \dots$

✎ *Given the first term and the common ratio of a geometric sequence find the first five terms and the explicit formula.*

5) $a_1 = 0.8, r = -5$

6) $a_1 = 1, r = 2$

✎ *Given the recursive formula for a geometric sequence find the common ratio, the first five terms, and the explicit formula.*

7) $a_n = a_{n-1}.2, a_1 = 2$

9) $a_n = a_{n-1}.5, a_1 = 2$

8) $a_n = a_{n-1}.-3, a_1 = -3$

10) $a_n = a_{n-1}.3, a_1 = -3$

✎ *Given two terms in a geometric sequence find the 8th term and the recursive formula.*

11) $a_4 = 12$ and $a_5 = -6$

12) $a_5 = 768$ and $a_2 = 12$

Chapter 13: Sequences and Series

Arithmetic Series

✒ *Find the first five terms of the sequence.*

1) $a_1 = 4, d = 5$ ____, ____, ____, ____, ____ .

2) $a_1 = -2, d = -3$ ____, ____, ____, ____, ____ .

3) $a_1 = 12, d = 7$ ____, ____, ____, ____, ____ .

4) $a_1 = 28, d = 12$ ____, ____, ____, ____, ____ .

5) $a_1 = 67, d = 13$ ____, ____, ____, ____, ____ .

6) $a_1 = 118, d = 85$ ____, ____, ____, ____, ____ .

7) $a_1 = -9, d = -16$ ____, ____, ____, ____, ____ .

8) $a_1 = -120, d = -100$ ____, ____, ____, ____, ____ .

9) $a_1 = 55, d = 23$ ____, ____, ____, ____, ____ .

10) $a_1 = 12.5, d = 4.2$ ____, ____, ____, ____, ____ .

✒ *Find the sum of the first four terms of the sequence.*

11) $a_3 = 12, d = 3$ 14) $a_8 = 38, d = 6$

12) $a_5 = 46, d = 5$ 15) $a_{12} = 88, d = 7$

13) $a_{10} = 66, d = 4$ 16) $a_{22} = 226, d = 9$

Finite Geometric Series

✍ **Evaluate the related series of each sequence.**

1) $-1, 5, -25, 125$

2) $-2, 6, -18, 54, -162$

3) $-1, 4, -16, 64$

4) $2, 12, 72, 432$

5) $-4, -8, -16, -32, -64$

6) $1, 5, 25, 125, 625$

✍ **Evaluate each geometric series described.**

7) $1 + 2 + 4 + 8 \ldots, n = 6$ _____

8) $1 - 4 + 16 - 64 \ldots, n = 9$ _____

9) $-2 - 6 - 18 - 54 \ldots, n = 9$ _____

10) $2 - 10 + 50 - 250 \ldots, n = 8$ _____

11) $1 - 5 + 25 - 125 \ldots, n = 7$ _____

12) $-3 - 6 - 12 - 24 \ldots, n = 9$ _____

13) $a_1 = -1, r = 4, n = 8$ _____

14) $a_1 = -2, r = -3, n = 9$ _____

15) $\sum_{n=1}^{8} 2 \cdot (-2)^{n-1}$ _____

16) $\sum_{n=1}^{9} 4 \cdot 3^{n-1}$ _____

17) $\sum_{n=1}^{10} 4 \cdot (-3)^{n-1}$ _____

18) $\sum_{m=1}^{9} -2^{m-1}$ _____

19) $\sum_{m=1}^{8} 3 \cdot 5^{m-1}$ _____

20) $\sum_{k=1}^{7} 2 \cdot 5^{k-1}$ _____

Chapter 13: Sequences and Series

Infinite Geometric Series

✎ *Determine if each geometric series converges or diverges.*

1) $a_1 = -3, r = 4$

2) $a_1 = 5.5, r = 0.5$

3) $a_1 = -1, r = 3$

4) $a_1 = 3.2, r = 0.2$

5) $a_1 = 5, r = 2$

6) $-1, 3, -9, 27, \dots$

7) $2, -1, \frac{1}{2}, -\frac{1}{4}, \frac{1}{8}, \dots$

8) $81 + 27 + 9 + 3 \dots$

9) $-3 + \frac{12}{5} - \frac{48}{25} + \frac{192}{125} \dots$

10) $\frac{128}{3,125} - \frac{64}{625} + \frac{32}{125} - \frac{16}{25} \dots$

✎ *Evaluate each infinite geometric series described.*

11) $a_1 = 3, r = -\frac{1}{5}$

12) $a_1 = 1, r = -3$

13) $a_1 = 1, r = -4$

14) $a_1 = 3, r = \frac{1}{2}$

15) $1 + 0.5 + 0.25 + 0.125 + \cdots$

16) $81 - 27 + 9 - 3 \dots,$

17) $1 - 0.6 + 0.36 - 0.216 \dots,$

18) $3 + \frac{9}{4} + \frac{27}{16} + \frac{81}{64} \dots,$

19) $\sum_{k=1}^{\infty} 4^{k-1}$

20) $\sum_{i=1}^{\infty} (\frac{1}{3})^{i-1}$

21) $\sum_{k=1}^{\infty} (-\frac{1}{3})^{k-1}$

22) $\sum_{n=1}^{\infty} 16(\frac{1}{4})^{n-1}$

Pascal's Triangle

✏️ *Use Pascal's triangle to expand the following binomial expressions.*

1) $(x + 6)^3$

2) $(1 + 3x)^2$

3) $(\sqrt{x} - \sqrt{3})^4$

4) $(1 - 5x)^5$

5) $(2x - 1)^3$

6) $(x + 4)^6$

7) $(y - 3x)^5$

8) $(y + 2)^7$

9) $(y - x)^9$

10) $(2x + y)^4$

✏️ *Solve.*

11) Determine the third element in the fourth row of Pascal's triangle.

12) Find the coefficients of expansions of $(x + y)^3$ using Pascal's triangle.

13) Find the sum of the elements in the 12th row of the Pascal's triangle.

14) Determine the elements in row 10 of Pascal's triangle.

15) Find the coefficients of expansions of $(x + y)^5$ using Pascal's triangle.

Binomial Theorem

✎ *Expand completely.*

1) $(2x - 1)^4 =$

2) $(x - y)^3 =$

3) $(x^4 - y)^5 =$

4) $(2x^3 + 1)^5 =$

5) $(y - x^2)^3 =$

6) $(y^3 - 4x)^3 =$

7) $(3x + 1)^4 =$

8) $(y - 3x)^3 =$

9) $(4x - 1)^4 =$

10) $(4x^3 + 4x)^4 =$

11) $(2x^2 - 1)^6 =$

12) $(1 + 3x^2)^4 =$

✎ *Solve.*

13) Write the 5th term of the expansion of $(1 - 4b^2)^4$. _____

14) Write the 2nd term of the expansion of $(1 - 3n^4)^4$. _____

15) Write the 5th term of the expansion of $(2 - 4y)^4$. _____

16) Write the 2nd term of the expansion of $(2x + y)^3$. _____

17) Write the 4th term of the expansion of $(4y + x)^4$. _____

18) Write the 4th term of the expansion of $(2x - 3)^5$. _____

Sigma Notation (Summation Notation)

✎ **Solve.**

1) $\sum_{n=1}^{7} 2a$

2) $\sum_{x=1}^{4} (50 - x)$

3) $\sum_{x=2}^{6} (100 - x)$

4) $\sum_{k=1}^{4} k(k + 3)$

5) $\sum_{n=1}^{5} (n^2 - 2)$

6) $\sum_{n=1}^{4} n^3$

7) $\sum_{k=1}^{3} \frac{k}{k+2}$

8) $\sum_{n=3}^{5} -\frac{2}{n}$

9) $\sum_{x=1}^{3} \frac{x^2}{x+2}$

10) $\sum_{n=2}^{6} (n^2 + n)$

11) $\sum_{i=3}^{7} \frac{i+2}{i-2}$

12) $\sum_{k=-3}^{3} (k^2 - k)$

13) $\sum_{k=1}^{4} k(k + 2)$

14) $\sum_{m=1}^{5} m$

15) $\sum_{n=1}^{7} (30 - n)$

16) $\sum_{a=4}^{9} (20 - a^2)$

17) $\sum_{n=1}^{4} (5n^2 + 4)$

18) $\sum_{k=0}^{4} (100 - k)$

19) $\sum_{m=1}^{6} \frac{m^2+1}{m}$

20) $\sum_{k=1}^{7} k^2$

Answers – Chapter 13

Arithmetic Sequences

1) $-5, -9, -13$
2) $7, 14, 21$
3) $18, 21, 24$
4) $24, 28, 32$
5) First Five Terms: $24, 26, 28, 30, 32$, Explicit: $a_n = 2n + 22$
6) First Five Terms: $-15, -20, -25, -30, -35$, Explicit: $a_n = -5n - 10$
7) First Five Terms: $18, 28, 38, 48, 58$, Explicit: $a_n = 10n + 8$
8) First Five Terms: $-38, -138, -238, -338, -438$, Explicit: $a_n = -100n + 62$
9) First Five Terms: $-31, -38, -45, -52, -59$, Explicit: $a_n = -7n - 24$
10) First Five Terms: $-39, -31, -23, -15, -7$, Explicit: $a_n = 8n - 47$
11) First Five Terms: $-12.5, -13.6, -14.7, -15.8, -16.9$, Explicit: $a_n = -1.1n - 11.4$
12) First Five Terms: $-21, -51, -81, -111, -141$, Explicit: $a_n = -30n + 9$
13) Next 3 terms: $-46, -48, -50$, Recursive: $a_n = a_{n-1} - 2, a_1 = -2$
14) Next 3 terms: $30.4, 32.2, 34$, Recursive: $a_n = a_{n-1} + 1.8, a_1 = 8.8$
15) Next 3 terms: $28.5, 29.6, 30.7$, Recursive: $a_n = a_{n-1} + 1.1, a_1 = 8.7$
16) Next 3 terms: $-0.8, -0.2, 0.4$, Recursive: $a_n = a_{n-1} + 0.6, a_1 = -13.4$

Geometric Sequences

1) $r = -5$
2) $r = 2$
3) not geometric
4) $r = 5$
5) First Five Terms: $0.8, -4, 20, -100, 500$
   Explicit: $a_n = 0.8 \cdot (-5)^{n-1}$
6) First Five Terms: $1, 2, 4, 8, 16$
Explicit: $a_n = 2^{n-1}$
7) Common Ratio: $r = 2$
First Five Terms: $2, 4, 8, 16, 32$
Explicit: $a_n = 2 \cdot 2^{n-1}$
8) Common Ratio: $r = -3$
First Five Terms: $-3, 9, -27, 81, -243$
Explicit: $a_n = -3 \cdot (-3)^{n-1}$

9) Common Ratio: $r = 5$
   First Five Terms: $10, 50, 250, 1,250$
   Explicit: $a_n = 2 \cdot 5^{n-1}$
10) Common Ratio: $r = 3$
   First Five Terms: $-3, -9, -27, -81, -243$
   Explicit: $a_n = -3 \cdot 3^{n-1}$
11) $a_8 = \frac{3}{4}$,
   Recursive: $a_n = a_{n-1} \cdot \frac{-1}{2}, a_1 = -96$
12) $a_8 = 49,152$,
   Recursive: $a_n = a_{n-1} \cdot 4, a_1 = 3$

Arithmetic Series

1) $4, 9, 14, 19, 24$

2) $-2, -5, -8, -11, -14$

3) $12, 19, 26, 33, 40$

4) $28, 40, 52, 64, 76$

5) $67, 80, 93, 106, 119$

6) $118, 203, 288, 373, 458$

7) $-9, -25, -41, -57, -73$

8) $-120, -220, -320, -420, -520$

9) $55, 78, 101, 124, 147$

10) $12.5, 16.7, 20.9, 25.1, 29.3$

11) 42

12) 134

13) 144

14) 20

15) 86

16) 202

Finite Geometric Series

1) 104

2) -122

3) 51

4) 518

5) -124

6) 781

7) 63

8) $52,429$

9) $-19,682$

10) $-130,208$

11) $13,021$

12) -1513

13) $-21,845$

14) $-9,842$

15) -170

16) $39,364$

17) -59048

18) -511

19) $292,968$

20) $39,062$

Infinite Geometric Series

1) Diverges

2) Converges

3) Diverges

4) Converges

5) Diverges

6) Diverges

7) Converges

8) Converges

9) Converges

10) Diverges

11) $\frac{5}{2}$

12) Infinite

13) Infinite

14) 6

15) 2

16) $\frac{243}{4}$

17) 0.625

18) 12

19) Infinite

20) $\frac{3}{2}$

21) $\frac{3}{4}$

22) $\frac{4}{3}$

Pascal's Triangle

1) $x^3 + 18x^2 + 108x + 216$

2) $1 + 6x + 9x^2$

3) $x^2 - 4\sqrt{3}x\sqrt{x} + 18x - 12\sqrt{3}\sqrt{x} + 9$

4) $1 - 25x + 250x^2 - 1250x^3 + 3125x^4 - 3125x^5$

5) $8x^3 - 12x^2 + 6x - 1$

6) $x^6 + 24x^5 + 240x^4 + 1{,}280x^3 + 3{,}840x^2 + 6{,}144x + 4{,}096$

7) $y^5 - 15y^4x + 90y^3x^2 - 270y^2x^3 + 405yx^4 - 243x^5$

8) $y^7 + 14y^6 + 84y^5 + 280y^4 + 560y^3 + 672y^2 + 448y + 128$

9) $y^9 - 9y^8x + 36y^7x^2 - 84y^6x^3 + 126y^5x^4 - 126y^4x^5 + 84y^3x^6 - 36y^2x^7 + 9yx^8 - x^9$

10) $16x^4 + 32x^3y + 24x^2y^2 + 8xy^3 + y^4$

11) 3

12) 1,3,3,1

13) 4,096

14) 1,9,36,84,126,126,84,36,9,1

15) 1,5,10,10,5,1

Binomial Theorem

1) $16x^4 - 32x^3 + 24x^2 - 8x + 1$

2) $x^3 - 3x^2y + 3xy^2 - y^3$

3) $x^{20} - 5x^{16}y + 10x^{12}y^{12} - 10x^8y^3 + 5x^4y^4 - y^5$

4) $32x^{15} + 80x^{12} + 80x^9 + 40x^6 + 10x^3 + 1$

5) $y^3 - 3y^2x^2 + 3yx^4 - x^6$

6) $y^9 - 12y^6x + 48y^3x^2 - 64x^3$

7) $81x^4 + 108x^3 + 54x^2 + 12x + 1$

8) $y^3 - 9y^2x + 27yx^2 - 27x^3$

9) $256x^4 - 256x^3 + 96x^2 - 16x + 1$

10) $256x^{12} + 1024x^{10} + 1536x^8 + 1024x^6 + 256x^4$

11) $64x^{12} - 192x^{10} + 240x^8 - 160x^6 + 60x^4 - 12x^2 + 1$

12) $1 + 12x^2 + 54x^4 + 108x^6 + 81x^8$

13) $256b^8$

14) $-12n^4$

15) $256y^4$

16) $12x^2y$

17) $16yx^3$

18) $-1,080x^2$

Sigma Notation (Summation Notation)

1) 56

2) 190

3) 480

4) 60

5) 45

6) 100

7) $1\frac{13}{30}$

8) $-\frac{47}{30}$

9) $\frac{47}{15}$

10) 110

11) $\frac{212}{15}$

12) 28

13) 50

14) 15

15) 182

16) -151

17) 166

18) 490

19) $\frac{469}{20}$

20) 140

Time to Test

Time to refine your math skill with a practice test.

In this book, there are five complete Algebra 2 Tests. Take these tests to simulate the test day experience. After you've finished, score your test using the answer keys.

Before You Start

- You'll need a pencil a calculator to take the test.

- For each question, there are five possible answers. Choose which one is best.

- It's okay to guess. There is no penalty for wrong answers.

- Use the answer sheet provided to record your answers.

- **Calculator is permitted for Algebra 2 Test.**

- After you've finished the test, review the answer key to see where you went wrong.

Good Luck!

College Algebra Practice Test 1

2024

Total number of questions: 60

Total time: No time limit

Calculator is permitted for College Algebra Math Test.

151

College Algebra Practice Test Answer Sheet

Remove (or photocopy) this answer sheet and use it to complete the practice test.

College Algebra Practice Test 1 Answer Sheet

#	Answer	#	Answer
1	Ⓐ Ⓑ Ⓒ Ⓓ Ⓔ	21	Ⓐ Ⓑ Ⓒ Ⓓ Ⓔ
2	Ⓐ Ⓑ Ⓒ Ⓓ Ⓔ	22	Ⓐ Ⓑ Ⓒ Ⓓ Ⓔ
3	Ⓐ Ⓑ Ⓒ Ⓓ Ⓔ	23	Ⓐ Ⓑ Ⓒ Ⓓ Ⓔ
4	Ⓐ Ⓑ Ⓒ Ⓓ Ⓔ	24	Ⓐ Ⓑ Ⓒ Ⓓ Ⓔ
5	Ⓐ Ⓑ Ⓒ Ⓓ Ⓔ	25	Ⓐ Ⓑ Ⓒ Ⓓ Ⓔ
6	Ⓐ Ⓑ Ⓒ Ⓓ Ⓔ	26	Ⓐ Ⓑ Ⓒ Ⓓ Ⓔ
7	Ⓐ Ⓑ Ⓒ Ⓓ Ⓔ	27	Ⓐ Ⓑ Ⓒ Ⓓ Ⓔ
8	Ⓐ Ⓑ Ⓒ Ⓓ Ⓔ	28	Ⓐ Ⓑ Ⓒ Ⓓ Ⓔ
9	Ⓐ Ⓑ Ⓒ Ⓓ Ⓔ	29	Ⓐ Ⓑ Ⓒ Ⓓ Ⓔ
10	Ⓐ Ⓑ Ⓒ Ⓓ Ⓔ	30	Ⓐ Ⓑ Ⓒ Ⓓ Ⓔ
11	Ⓐ Ⓑ Ⓒ Ⓓ Ⓔ	31	Ⓐ Ⓑ Ⓒ Ⓓ Ⓔ
12	Ⓐ Ⓑ Ⓒ Ⓓ Ⓔ	32	Ⓐ Ⓑ Ⓒ Ⓓ Ⓔ
13	Ⓐ Ⓑ Ⓒ Ⓓ Ⓔ	33	Ⓐ Ⓑ Ⓒ Ⓓ Ⓔ
14		34	Ⓐ Ⓑ Ⓒ Ⓓ Ⓔ
15	Ⓐ Ⓑ Ⓒ Ⓓ Ⓔ	35	Ⓐ Ⓑ Ⓒ Ⓓ Ⓔ
16	Ⓐ Ⓑ Ⓒ Ⓓ Ⓔ	36	Ⓐ Ⓑ Ⓒ Ⓓ Ⓔ
17	Ⓐ Ⓑ Ⓒ Ⓓ Ⓔ	37	Ⓐ Ⓑ Ⓒ Ⓓ Ⓔ
18	Ⓐ Ⓑ Ⓒ Ⓓ Ⓔ	38	Ⓐ Ⓑ Ⓒ Ⓓ Ⓔ
19	Ⓐ Ⓑ Ⓒ Ⓓ Ⓔ	39	Ⓐ Ⓑ Ⓒ Ⓓ Ⓔ
20		40	Ⓐ Ⓑ Ⓒ Ⓓ Ⓔ

1) Which value of x is the rational part of the solution to the equation $4x^2 - 9 = 12x$?

    A. $x = \frac{3}{2}$

    B. $x = -\frac{3}{2}$

    C. $x = 3$ and -3

    D. $x = -\frac{1}{2}$ and $x = \frac{1}{2}$

    E. $x = -\frac{3}{2}$ and $x = \frac{3}{2}$

2) What is the solution to this equation?
$$5(x - 3) - 2(x + 5) = -13$$

    A. -3

    B. 2

    C. 3

    D. 4

    E. 5

3) Which inequality can be represented by the graph below?

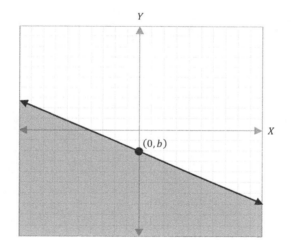

    A. $2y \leq -(x + b)$

    B. $x + 2y \leq 2b$

    C. $x - y \geq b$

    D. $2x - y \geq b$

    E. $x - y \leq b$

4) Which expression is equivalent to $(2n - 5)(3n + 4)$?

    A. $6n^2 - 7n - 20$

    B. $6n^2 - n - 20$

    C. $6n^2 + n - 20$

    D. $5n^2 - 7n - 20$

    E. $5n^2 - n - 20$

5) Given $g(x) = x^2 - 49$, which statement is true?

    A. The only zero, 7, can be found when $0 = (x - 7)(x - 7)$.

    B. The only zero, 49, can be found when $0 = (x - 49)(x - 49)$.

    C. The zeros, -7 and 7, can be found when $0 = (x + 7)(x - 7)$.

    D. The zeros, -49 and 49, can be found when $0 = (x + 49)(x - 49)$.

    E. The only zero, -7, can be found when $0 = (x + 7)(x + 7)$.

6) What is the range of the function shown below?

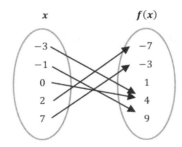

    A. $\{-3, -1, 1, 0, 2, 7\}$

    B. $\{-3, -1, 0, 2, 7\}$

    C. $\{-7, -3, 1, 4, 9\}$

    D. $\{1\}$

    E. $\{-7, -3, 4, 9\}$

7) Which graph does not represent y as a function of x?

A.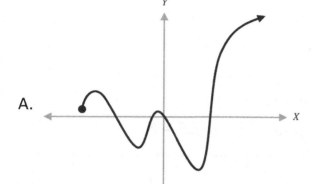

B.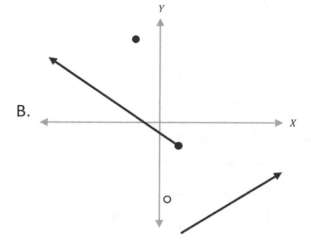

C.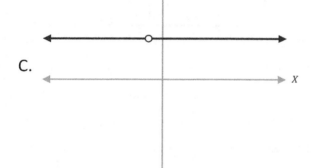

D.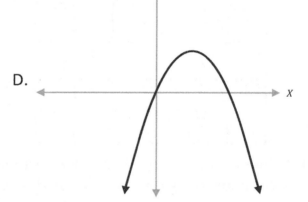

E.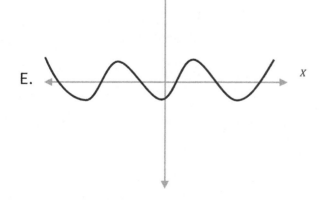

8) What is the positive solution to $2x^2 + 5x - 3 = 0$?

    A. $\frac{1}{2}$

    B. 3

    C. $\frac{1}{2}$ and 3

    D. $\frac{1}{2}$ and $\frac{1}{3}$

    E. 2 and 3

9) Which table shows the same relationship as $y = 5x - 3x^2 + 2$?

A.

x	-2	-1	0	2	3
y	-20	-6	4	0	-1

B.

x	-2	-1	0	2	3
y	-20	-6	2	0	-10

C.

x	-2	-1	0	2	3
y	-20	4	2	0	-1

D.

x	-2	-1	0	2	3
y	-20	4	4	0	-10

D.

x	-2	-1	0	2	3
y	-20	4	2	0	-10

10) The function $y = x^2 + 2x - 8$ is graphed below.
What are the values of x when $x^2 + 2x - 8 = -5$?

    A. $x = -5$ and $x = 8$

    B. $x = -4$ and $x = 2$

    C. $x = -4$ and $x = 1$

    D. $x = -3$ and $x = 2$

    E. $x = -3$ and $x = 1$

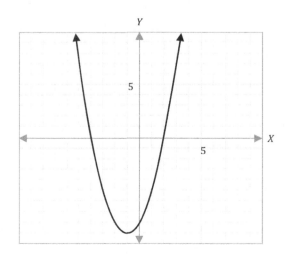

11) The slope and y−intercept of the graph of f were changed to make the graph of g, as shown below.

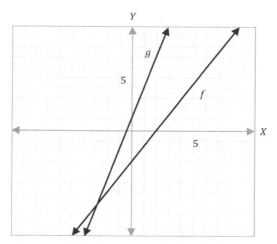

Which statement describes the changes that were made to the graph of f to make the graph of g?

A. The slope was multiplied by -2, and the y−intercept was decreased by 4 to make the graph of g.

B. The slope was multiplied by $-\frac{1}{2}$, and the y−intercept was decreased by 4 to make the graph of g.

C. The slope was multiplied by 2, and the y−intercept was increased by 4 to make the graph of g.

D. The slope was multiplied by $\frac{1}{2}$, and the y−intercept was increased by 4 to make the graph of g.

E. The slope was multiplied by -2, and the y−intercept was increased by 4 to make the graph of g.

12) A table of values for the exponential function g is shown below.

x	$g(x)$
1	10,000
2	9,750
3	9,506
4	9,269
5	9,037

Which situation could describe this function?

A. The value of a car increases by approximately $2\frac{1}{2}\%$ per year.

B. The value of a house increases by \$250 per year.

C. The value of a house increases by $2\frac{1}{4}\%$ per year.

D. The value of a house decreases by approximately $2\frac{1}{2}\%$ per year.

E. The value of a house decreases by \$250 per year.

13) Which expression is equivalent to $(yx + 7z - 2xy) - (3xy - z)$?
   A. $4xy + 8z$
   B. $8z - 4xy$
   C. $4(z - xy)$
   D. $yx + 8z - 5xy$
   E. $8z + 4xy$

14) If $x^2 + 6x + r$ factors into $(x + 2)(x + p)$, and r and p are constants, what is the value of r?

15) If $f(x) = 3x + 4(x + 1) + 2$ then $f(4x) =$

   A. $28x + 6$

   B. $16x - 6$

   C. $25x + 4$

   D. $12x + 3$

   D. $24x + 6$

16) What is the solution to the system of equations below?

$$3x + y = 15$$
$$-2x + 4y = 10$$

   A. $\left(\frac{25}{7}, \frac{7}{30}\right)$

   B. $\left(\frac{25}{7}, \frac{30}{7}\right)$

   C. $\left(\frac{7}{25}, \frac{30}{7}\right)$

   D. There is no solution.

   E. There is an infinite number of solutions.

17) The complete graph of function f is shown in the $xy-$plane below. For what value of x is the value of $f(x)$ at its minimum?

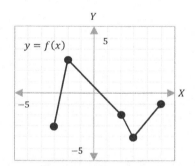

   A. -3

   B. -2

   C. 2

   D. 3

   E. 5

18) What is the solution to $1 + 3(m - 4) = 7m$?

   A. $m = -11$

   B. $m = 2.75$

   C. $m = -2.25$

   D. $m = 11$

   E. $m = -2.75$

19) The graph of the quadratic function g passes through the points $(-3,0)$, $(-1,4)$, $(0,3)$, and $(2,-5)$. Which of the following shows the same relationship as g?

A. $g(x) = x^2 + 2x - 3$

B.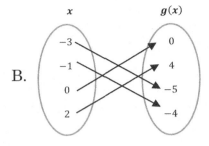

C.

x	$g(x)$
0	-3
4	-1
4	0
-5	2

D.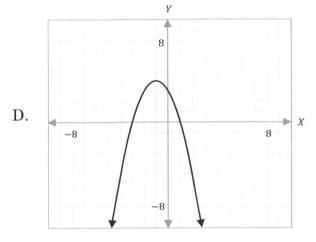

E. $g(x) = 2x^2 + x - 19$

20) The function f is shown in the figure below. The function g is perpendicular to the function f at the point $(0,4)$. What is the value of x on the point where the function g meets the x −axis?

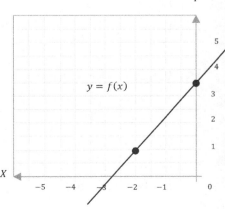

21) Where defined $\dfrac{\frac{x+3}{x^2-9}}{\frac{x-2}{x-3}}$?

   A. $\dfrac{1}{(x-2)}$

   B. $\dfrac{1}{(x-3)(x+3)}$

   C. $\dfrac{(x-3)}{(x-2)}$

   D. $\dfrac{1}{(x+3)(x-2)}$

   E. $\dfrac{(x+3)(x-3)}{(x-2)}$

22) Which of the lines in the following figure is the graph of $x = -3$?

   A. A

   B. B

   C. C

   D. D

   E. E

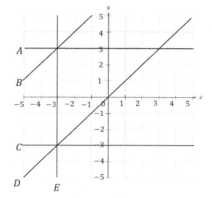

23) Which of the following graphs represents the solution of $|9 + 6x| \le 3$?

   A.
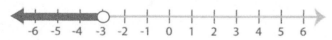

   B.

   C.

   D.
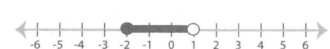

   E.

24) What are all real values of a in the following equation?

$$\frac{a}{4} + \frac{1}{2} = \frac{3}{a-2}$$

A. $a = 4$

B. $a = 2, a = 4$

C. $a = 2, a = 6$

D. $a = -4, a = 4$

E. $a = 4, a = 8$

25) The graph of $y = f(x)$ is shown in the xy−plane below. Which the following equations could define $f(x)$?

A. $x^2 + 2x - 3$

B. $-x^2 - 2x + 3$

C. $(x-2)(x+3)$

D. $(x-1)^2 + 3$

E. $(x+1)^2 + 3$

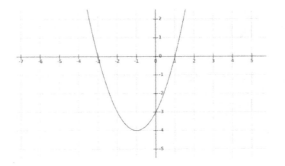

26) The shaded region in the figure below represents the intersection of the graphs of $x \geq 0$, $y \geq 0$, and which of the following inequalities?

A. $y \geq 2x - 1$

B. $y \leq x + 2$

C. $y \geq x + 2$

D. $y \geq x - 2$

E. $y \geq -2x + 1$

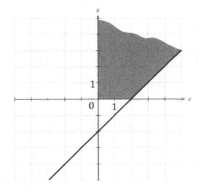

27) Which of the following is not an equivalent statement?

A. $x^{-2} = \frac{1}{x^2}$

B. $(x^2)^3 = x^6$

C. $x^6 - 5x^2 = x^2(x^3 - 5)$

D. $\left(3 - \frac{a}{6}\right)\left(3 + \frac{a}{6}\right) = 9 - \frac{a^2}{36}$

E. $4x^2 - 16x + 8 = (2x - 4)^2$

28) What is the simplified form of $\sqrt{3}(\sqrt{3} - 4)$?

A. $4 - \sqrt{3}$

B. $3 - 4\sqrt{3}$

C. $1 - 3\sqrt{3}$

D. $3 - \sqrt{3}$

E. $\sqrt{3} - 4$

29) If $h(x) = x + 8$ and $g(x) = 3x^2 + 24x$, what is the value of $\left(\frac{g}{h}\right)(x)$?

A. $3x + 8$

B. $x - 3$

C. $x + 8$

D. $3x$

E. $\frac{3x+24}{x+8}$

30) Find the perimeter of the figure.

A. $4x + 5y$

B. $3x + 5$

C. $9y - 2$

D. $9x + 3y$

E. $x + y + 5$

31) Write the following polynomial in standard form. $\frac{12x^2+8x^3+24}{4}$

    A. $3x^3 + 2x^2 + 6$

    B. $2x^3 + 3x^2 + 6$

    C. $2x^2 + 4x^3 + 4$

    D. $x^3 + 2x^2 + 3$

    E. $2x^3 + 3x^2 + 8$

32) Rewrite $(-5)^{-3}$ with positive exponents.

    A. 125

    B. -125

    C. $-\frac{1}{125}$

    D. $\frac{1}{125}$

    E. $-\frac{1}{25}$

33) Find the expanded form of $\log \frac{a^2 b^2}{c^4}$.

    A. $\log ab - 4\log c$

    B. $2\log a + 2\log b - 4\log c$

    C. $2\log ab - 4\log c$

    D. $\log \frac{a}{c} + \log \frac{b}{c}$

    E. $2\log a - 2\log b + 4\log c$

34) What is the domain of the function $g(x) = \frac{3x}{x^2-9}$.

    A. All real numbers

    B. All real numbers except 3

    C. All real numbers except -3

    D. All real numbers except 0

    E. All real numbers except 3 and -3

35) Classify $-8x^2 + 5x^4 + 9 - 3x^3$ by degree.

    A. constant

    B. linear

    C. quadratic

    D. cubic

    E. quartic

36) What is the vertex of the parabola $y = (x + 9)^2 - 5$?

    A. $(9, 5)$

    B. $(-1, -9)$

    C. $(-9, 1)$

    D. $(-9, -5)$

    E. $(5, -9)$

37) Find the area of a square whose sides are $1 + \sqrt{6}$.

    A. $2 + \sqrt{5}$

    B. $1 - \sqrt{6}$

    C. $2\sqrt{6}$

    D. $2 - \sqrt{6}$

    E. $7 + 2\sqrt{6}$

38) Which of the following shows a rule for the following sequence? $5, 9, 13, 17, \ldots$

    A. $a_n = 4n$

    B. $a_n = n - 4$

    C. $a_n = 4n - 6$

    D. $a_n = 4n + 1$

    E. $a_n = n + 4$

39) What is the inverse of $g(x) = 5x - 7$?

 A. $g^{-1}(x) = \frac{x+7}{5}$

 B. $g^{-1}(x) = \frac{x+5}{7}$

 C. $g^{-1}(x) = \frac{x}{5} + 7$

 D. $g^{-1}(x) = x + 7$

 E. $g^{-1}(x) = \frac{x-7}{5}$

40) Solve the following quadratic equation by using quadratic formula.
$$x^2 + 7x + 6 = 0$$

 A. $-\sqrt{8}, -1$

 B. $\sqrt{5}, -2$

 C. $-6, -1$

 D. $-\sqrt{5}, -2$

 E. $6, -1$

End of College Algebra Practice Test 1   STOP

College Algebra Practice Test 2

2024

Total number of questions: 40

Total time: No time limit

Calculator is permitted for College Algebra Math Test.

167

College Algebra Practice Test Answer Sheet

Remove (or photocopy) this answer sheet and use it to complete the practice test.

#		#	
1	Ⓐ Ⓑ Ⓒ Ⓓ Ⓔ	21	Ⓐ Ⓑ Ⓒ Ⓓ Ⓔ
2	Ⓐ Ⓑ Ⓒ Ⓓ Ⓔ	22	Ⓐ Ⓑ Ⓒ Ⓓ Ⓔ
3	Ⓐ Ⓑ Ⓒ Ⓓ Ⓔ	23	Ⓐ Ⓑ Ⓒ Ⓓ Ⓔ
4	Ⓐ Ⓑ Ⓒ Ⓓ Ⓔ	24	Ⓐ Ⓑ Ⓒ Ⓓ Ⓔ
5	Ⓐ Ⓑ Ⓒ Ⓓ Ⓔ	25	Ⓐ Ⓑ Ⓒ Ⓓ Ⓔ
6	Ⓐ Ⓑ Ⓒ Ⓓ Ⓔ	26	Ⓐ Ⓑ Ⓒ Ⓓ Ⓔ
7	Ⓐ Ⓑ Ⓒ Ⓓ Ⓔ	27	Ⓐ Ⓑ Ⓒ Ⓓ Ⓔ
8	Ⓐ Ⓑ Ⓒ Ⓓ Ⓔ	28	Ⓐ Ⓑ Ⓒ Ⓓ Ⓔ
9	Ⓐ Ⓑ Ⓒ Ⓓ Ⓔ	29	Ⓐ Ⓑ Ⓒ Ⓓ Ⓔ
10	Ⓐ Ⓑ Ⓒ Ⓓ Ⓔ	30	Ⓐ Ⓑ Ⓒ Ⓓ Ⓔ
11	Ⓐ Ⓑ Ⓒ Ⓓ Ⓔ	31	Ⓐ Ⓑ Ⓒ Ⓓ Ⓔ
12	Ⓐ Ⓑ Ⓒ Ⓓ Ⓔ	32	Ⓐ Ⓑ Ⓒ Ⓓ Ⓔ
13	Ⓐ Ⓑ Ⓒ Ⓓ Ⓔ	33	Ⓐ Ⓑ Ⓒ Ⓓ Ⓔ
14		34	Ⓐ Ⓑ Ⓒ Ⓓ Ⓔ
15	Ⓐ Ⓑ Ⓒ Ⓓ Ⓔ	35	Ⓐ Ⓑ Ⓒ Ⓓ Ⓔ
16	Ⓐ Ⓑ Ⓒ Ⓓ Ⓔ	36	Ⓐ Ⓑ Ⓒ Ⓓ Ⓔ
17	Ⓐ Ⓑ Ⓒ Ⓓ Ⓔ	37	Ⓐ Ⓑ Ⓒ Ⓓ Ⓔ
18	Ⓐ Ⓑ Ⓒ Ⓓ Ⓔ	38	Ⓐ Ⓑ Ⓒ Ⓓ Ⓔ
19	Ⓐ Ⓑ Ⓒ Ⓓ Ⓔ	39	Ⓐ Ⓑ Ⓒ Ⓓ Ⓔ
20		40	Ⓐ Ⓑ Ⓒ Ⓓ Ⓔ

1) The function $g(x)$ is defined by a polynomial. Some values of x and $g(x)$ are shown in the table below. Which of the following must be a factor of $g(x)$?

x	$g(x)$
-1	0
0	2
1	-5
5	0

A. $x + 1$
B. $x - 2$
C. $x + 2$
D. $x + 5$
E. x

2) If 29 wooden sheets were stacked on top of each other in a column, the column would be approximately $60\frac{3}{5}$ centimeters tall. At this rate, which of the following is closest to the number of wooden sheets it would take to make a 122-centimeter-tall column?
A. 40
B. 59
C. 80
D. 95
E. 110

3) The formula below shows the relation between the temperature of food inside a microwave a and the time that takes to heat food up b. Which of the following expresses the time in terms of the temperature of food? $a = 2.35b + 29$
A. $b = \frac{a - 2.35}{29}$
B. $b = \frac{29 - a}{2.35}$
C. $b = \frac{2.35}{a - 29}$
D. $b = \frac{2.35}{a + 29}$
E. $b = \frac{a - 29}{2.35}$

4) The set of ordered pairs below represents some points on the graph of function f.
$$\{(3,2), (0,-1), (-2,7), (-1,2), (5,14)\}$$
What is the parent function of f?
A. $y = x$
B. $y = x^2$
C. $y = 3^x$
D. $y = \sqrt{x}$
E. $y = \frac{1}{x}$

5) A basketball player scored at least 15 points more than the previous record for the most points scored in a game. Which inequality can be used to find all possible values of p, the number of points the player scored, in terms of r, the previous record?
A. $p \leq r - 15$
B. $p \geq r + 15$
C. $p \leq r + 15$
D. $p \leq 2r$
E. $p \geq 2r + 15$

6) An engineer is designing a suspension bridge with n sections. The length of each section is $48.2m$. The bridge will also have two towers, each of which is $125.6m$ tall. Which function can be used to find the total length of the bridge in meters, including the towers?
A. $L(x) = 48.2n + 125.6$
B. $L(x) = 251.2 - 48.2n$
C. $L(x) = 48.2n - 125.6$
D. $L(x) = 173.8n$
E. $L(x) = 251.2 + 48.2n$

7) The cost of shipping a package varies directly with its weight. The cost of shipping a 4-pound package is $10.80. What is the cost, in dollars, of shipping a 2.5-pound package?
A. $6.75
B. $8.50
C. $5.40
D. $3.60
E. $2.40

8) What are the x −intercepts of the graph of the quadratic function $g(x) = -3x^2 + 9x - 6$?
   A. $(-1,0)$ and $(3,0)$
   B. $(-2,0)$ and $(2,0)$
   C. $(-1,0)$ and $(2,0)$
   D. $(1,0)$ and $(2,0)$
   E. $(1,0)$ and $(-2,0)$

9) Which of the following is equivalent to $8^{\frac{2}{5}}$?
   A. $\sqrt[2]{8}$
   B. $\sqrt[5]{8}$
   C. $4\sqrt{2}$
   D. $2\sqrt[5]{2}$
   E. $2\sqrt{2}$

10) The graph of $y = -3x^2 + 12x + 6$ is shown below. If the graph crosses the y −axis at the point $(0, r)$, what is the value of r?
   A. 2
   B. 3
   C. 6
   D. 9
   E. 12

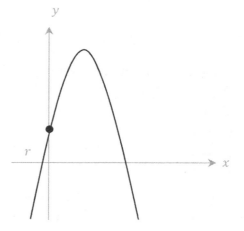

11) A helicopter delivers only 100-pound packages and 120-pound packages. For each delivery trip, the helicopter must carry at least 10 packages, and the total weight of the packages can be at most 1,100 pounds. What is the maximum number of 120-pound packages that the helicopter can carry per trip?
   A. 2
   B. 4
   C. 5
   D. 6
   E. 7

12) What is the equation of the line that has a slope of 2 and passes through the point (3,5)?
A. $y = 2x - 6$
B. $y = 2x + 1$
C. $x = 2y - 1$
D. $x = 2y + 1$
E. $y = 2x - 1$

13) The graph of an equation in the form $y = mx + b$ is shown on the grid.

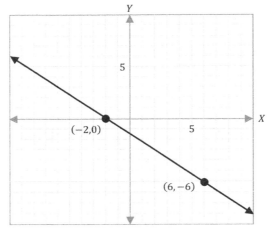

Based on the graph, what is the value of x when $y = 3$?
A. 3
B. 6
C. −3
D. −6
E. −7

14) The line k is parallel to the line $y = \frac{3}{4}x + 3$ and intersects the y−axis at point −7. If point $m(12, b)$ is on the line k, what is the value of b?

15) Which of the following equation relates y to x for the values in the table below?

A. $y = \frac{1}{2}x + \frac{3}{5}$

B. $y = \frac{3}{5}x + 2$

C. $y = \left(\frac{1}{2}\right)^x + \frac{2}{5}$

D. $y = \left(\frac{1}{3}\right)^{\frac{3}{5}x}$

E. $y = \frac{1}{2}x - \frac{3}{5}$

x	y
2	$\frac{8}{5}$
3	$\frac{21}{10}$
4	$\frac{13}{5}$
5	$\frac{31}{10}$

16) A boutique store has a total of 200 dresses on display. The ratio of the number of evening dresses to the number of cocktail dresses on display is $3:5$. How many evening and cocktail dresses are on display?

A. 50 evening dresses and 150 cocktail dresses

B. 75 evening dresses and 125 cocktail dresses

C. 90 evening dresses and 110 cocktail dresses

D. 100 evening dresses and 100 cocktail dresses

E. 110 evening dresses and 120 cocktail dresses

17) The total cost of renting a bicycle from a rental shop is a function of the number of hours the bicycle is rented. The owner of the rental shop charges \$10 per hour up to a maximum of 5 hours plus a \$15 late fee. What is the greatest value in the range for this situation?

A. 75

B. 65

C. 60

D. 50

E. 45

18) A small town's average monthly electricity consumption is 500 kilowatt-hours (kWh). In the first six months of this year, the town consumed a total of $2,800kWh$. If it is expected to consume between 400 and $550kWh$ per month for the rest of the year, what is a reasonable number of additional months needed for the town to reach its average annual electricity consumption?

A. 3 months

B. 4 months

C. 5 months

D. 6 months

E. 7 months

19) Which expression is equivalent to $5a\left(\frac{1}{5}a - 2\right) - 2\left(4 - \frac{5}{2}a\right)$?
    A. $a^2 + 5a + 8$
    B. $a^2 + 5a - 8$
    C. $a^2 - 5a + 8$
    D. $a^2 - 5a - 8$
    E. $a^2 - 8a - 5$

20) Kilometers and miles are units of measure of length. They are directly proportional such that 10 miles are equal to 16 kilometers. How much length, in kilometers, is equal to 50 miles?

21) What is the value of x in this equation?
$$4\sqrt{2x + 9} = 28$$

    A. 7
    B. 14
    C. 20
    D. 28
    E. 40

22) The table represents different values of function $g(x)$. What is the value of $3g(-2) - 2g(3)$?

   A. -2

   B. 3

   C. -12

   D. 13

   E. 18

x	$g(x)$
-2	3
-1	2
0	1
1	0
2	-1
3	-2

23) What is the equation of the following graph?

   A. $y = |x| - 1$

   B. $y = |x| + 1$

   C. $y = -|x| + 1$

   D. $y = |x + 1|$

   E. $y = |x - 1|$

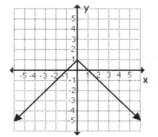

24) What is the sum of $\sqrt{x-7}$ and $\sqrt{x} - 7$ when $\sqrt{x} = 4$?

   A. 0

   B. -1

   C. 3

   D. -3

   E. 6

25) In a right triangle $\sin A = \frac{1}{3}$, what is $\cos A$?

   A. 1

   B. $\frac{1}{2}$

   C. $\frac{\sqrt{3}}{2}$

   D. $\frac{\sqrt{8}}{3}$

   E. $\sqrt{3}$

26) If $(x - 2)^2 + 1 > 3x - 1$, then x can equal which of the following?

    A. 1

    B. 3

    C. 4

    D. 6

    E. 8

27) Solve for x: $\frac{3x}{5} = 27$?

    A. 16.2

    B. 31

    C. 45

    D. 55

    E. 135

28) What is the solution of the equation $81 = 3^{2x}$?

    A. $\frac{1}{2}$

    B. $\frac{3}{2}$

    C. $\frac{5}{2}$

    D. 1

    E. 2

29) $(2i - 3) - (2 - i)(i - 2) =$

    A. $2i$

    B. $-2i$

    C. $2i - 1$

    D. $-2i + 1$

    E. $-2i - 1$

30) If $f(x) = \frac{4x^2 - 6x + 12}{9 - x}$, which of the following is NOT defined?

  A. $f(0)$

  B. $f(-4)$

  C. $f(-6)$

  D. $f(9)$

  E. $f(-9)$

31) Find the solution (x, y) to the following system of equations?
$$-3x - y = 6$$
$$6x + 4y = 10$$

  A. $(14, 5)$

  B. $(6, 8)$

  C. $(11, 17)$

  D. $(-\frac{17}{3}, 11)$

  E. $(-6, 11)$

32) $\frac{3x-2}{x-3} - \frac{x-4}{3x-2} =$

  A. $\frac{(3x-2)}{(x-3)}$

  B. $\frac{(x-4)}{(x-3)}$

  C. $\frac{8x^2 - 5x - 8}{(x-3)(3x-2)}$

  D. $\frac{8x^2 - 13x + 16}{(x-3)(3x-2)}$

  E. $\frac{10x^2 - 19x + 16}{(x-3)(3x-2)}$

33) What is the sum of all values of n that satisfies $2n^2 + 16n + 24 = 0$?

  A. 4

  B. -4

  C. 8

  D. -8

  E. -12

34) For $i = \sqrt{-1}$, what is the value of $\frac{3+2i}{5+i}$?

   A. i

   B. $\frac{32i}{5}$

   C. $\frac{7+7i}{13}$

   D. $\frac{17+7i}{26}$

   E. $\frac{17-i}{5}$

35) Which of the point in the below figure represents the complex number $2 - 4i$?

   A. A

   B. B

   C. C

   D. D

   E. E

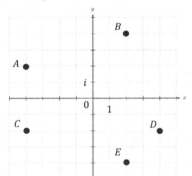

36) If $2x - 5y = 10$, what is x in terms of y?

   A. $x = \frac{5}{2}y + 5$

   B. $x = \frac{2}{5}y + 10$

   C. $x = -\frac{5}{2}y - 5$

   D. $x = -\frac{5}{2}y + 5$

   E. $x = -\frac{2}{5}y + 5$

37) Which of the following is equivalent to $\frac{x+(5x)^2+(3x)^3}{x}$?

   A. $16x^2 + 25x$

   B. $16x^3 - 16x^2 + 1$

   C. $16x^2 + 25x + 1$

   D. $27x^3 + 16x^2 + 1$

   E. $27x^2 + 25x + 1$

38) What is the range of the function shown below?

A. $-4 \leq x \leq 3$

B. $-4 \leq y \leq 3$

C. $-4 \leq x \leq 4$

D. $-4 \leq y \leq 4$

E. $-2 \leq y \leq 4$

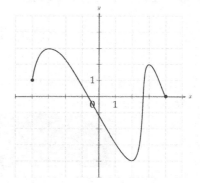

39) If $tan\, x = \frac{8}{15}$, then $sin\, x =$

A. $\frac{7}{15}$

B. $\frac{8}{17}$

C. $\frac{1}{2}$

D. $\frac{15}{17}$

E. It cannot be determined from the information given.

40) In which direction does the graph of the parabola $y = -6x^2$ open?

A. Right

B. Left

C. Up

D. Down

E. Given information is not enough.

End of College Algebra Practice Test 2 | **STOP**

College Algebra Practice Tests Answers and Explanations

Now, it's time to review your results to see where you went wrong and what areas you need to improve.

College Algebra Practice Test 1				College Algebra Practice Test 2			
1	E	21	A	1	A	21	C
2	D	22	C	2	B	22	D
3	B	23	E	3	E	23	C
4	A	24	D	4	B	24	A
5	C	25	A	5	B	25	D
6	E	26	D	6	E	26	E
7	B	27	E	7	A	27	C
8	A	28	B	8	D	28	E
9	B	29	D	9	D	29	B
10	E	30	D	10	C	30	D
11	C	31	B	11	C	31	D
12	D	32	C	12	E	32	C
13	B	33	B	13	D	33	D
14	8	34	E	14	2	34	D
15	A	35	E	15	A	35	E
16	B	36	D	16	B	36	A
17	D	37	E	17	B	37	B
18	E	38	D	18	A	38	B
19	D	39	A	19	D	39	B
20	6	40	C	20	80	40	D

College Algebra Practice Test 1

Answers and Explanations

1) Choice E is correct

To solve the equation $4x^2 - 9 = 12x$, we can start by bringing all the terms to one side of the equation, so that we have: $4x^2 - 12x - 9 = 0$.

Next, we can use the quadratic formula to find the values of x that satisfy this equation. The quadratic formula is:

$$x_{1,2} = \frac{-b \pm \sqrt{b^2 - 4ac}}{2a}$$

For our equation, we have $a = 4$, $b = -12$, and $c = -9$. Substituting these values into the quadratic formula, we get:

$$x_{1,2} = \frac{-(-12) \pm \sqrt{(-12)^2 - 4(4)(-9)}}{2(4)} \rightarrow x_{1,2} = \frac{12 \pm \sqrt{144 + 144}}{8}$$

$$\rightarrow x_{1,2} = \frac{12 \pm 12\sqrt{2}}{8} = \frac{3 \pm 3\sqrt{2}}{2}$$

Therefore, the solutions to the equation $4x^2 - 9 = 12x$ are $x_1 = \frac{3+3\sqrt{2}}{2}$ and $x_2 = \frac{3-3\sqrt{2}}{2}$.

So, the rational part of the solution is $\frac{3}{2}$ and $-\frac{3}{2}$.

2) Choice D is correct

First, distribute the 2 and 5: $5x - 15 - 2x - 10 = -13$. Combine like terms: $3x - 25 = -13$. Add 25 to both sides: $3x = 12$. Divide both sides by 3: $x = 4$. The solution is $x = 4$, which corresponds to option D.

3) Choice B is correct

To find the inequality that represents the graph of the problem, we first get the equation of the line passing through points $(2b, 0)$ and $(0, b)$ based on the graph, such that the number b is negative. The slope of the line passing through (x_1, y_1) and (x_2, y_2): $m = \frac{y_2 - y_1}{x_2 - x_1}$. So, for the points $(2b, 0)$ and $(0, b)$, we get:

$$m = \frac{b - 0}{0 - 2b} = -\frac{b}{2b} = -\frac{1}{2}.$$

Then, write the equation of the line passes through the point $(0, b)$ with the slope $m = -\frac{1}{2}$:

$y - b = -\frac{1}{2}(x - 0) \rightarrow y = -\frac{1}{2}x + b$.

We can rewrite the equation as below: $x + 2y = 2b$. Next, put some points like (b, b) of the shaded area in the equation of the function to get the direction of the inequality.

(b, b): $b + 2(b) = 3b$, we know that b is negative, then $3b < 2b$. Answer set, therefore the equation of the inequality is $x + 2y \leq 2b$.

4) Choice A is correct

To expand the expression $(2n - 5)(3n + 4)$, we can use the distributive property of multiplication:

$(2n - 5)(3n + 4) = 2n \times 3n + 2n \times 4 - 5 \times 3n - 5 \times 4$.

Simplifying, we get:

$2n \times 3n + 2n \times 4 - 5 \times 3n - 5 \times 4 = 6n^2 + 8n - 15n - 20$.

Combining like terms, we get:

$6n^2 + 8n - 15n - 20 = 6n^2 - 7n - 20$.

Therefore, the expression that is equivalent to $(2n - 5)(3n + 4)$ is $6n^2 - 7n - 20$.

5) Choice C is correct

The given function is $g(x) = x^2 - 49$, which can be factored as $0 = (x + 7)(x - 7)$. Therefore, the zeros of the function are $x = -7$ and $x = 7$.

Option C is correct because it shows the correct factorization of the function and the corresponding zeros. Options A, B and E both show a repeated factorization which is incorrect. Option D shows a different factorization with zeros that don't match the zeros of the function.

6) Choice E is correct

The range of a function is the set of output values, which is $f(x)$ here. Therefore, we have:

$\{-7, -3, 4, 9\}$

Note that no input value of the function gives an output of 1.

7) Choice B is correct

We check the graphs to find a choice that intersects the vertical lines parallel to the y −axis of the graph at least at one point of the domain of the graph in more than one point.

Graph B is not a function because there are two output values for the graph at the specified location.

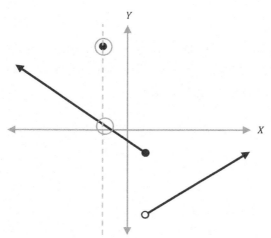

8) Choice A is correct

To solve the equation $2x^2 + 5x - 3 = 0$, we can use the quadratic formula, which states that if $ax^2 + bx + c = 0$, then:

$$x_{1,2} = \frac{-b \pm \sqrt{b^2 - 4ac}}{2a}$$

Plugging in $a = 2$, $b = 5$, and $c = -3$, we get:

$$x_{1,2} = \frac{-5 \pm \sqrt{5^2 - 4(2)(-3)}}{2(2)} \rightarrow x_{1,2} = \frac{-5 \pm \sqrt{49}}{4} \rightarrow x_{1,2} = \frac{-5 \pm 7}{4}.$$

So, the solutions to the equation are $x_1 = -3$ and $x_2 = \frac{1}{2}$. Since we're looking for a positive solution, the answer is $x = \frac{1}{2}$.

9) Choice B is correct

The function $y = 5x - 3x^2 + 2$ is quadratic. So, the domain y is all real numbers. According to the information in the table, the input values are the set $\{-2, -1, 0, 2, 3\}$. We evaluate the y −values of the given function as:

$x = -2$: $y = 5(-2) - 3(-2)^2 + 2 = -20$

$x = -1$: $y = 5(-1) - 3(-1)^2 + 2 = -6$

$x = 0$: $y = 5(0) - 3(0)^2 + 2 = 2$

$x = 2$: $y = 5(2) - 3(2)^2 + 2 = 0$

$x = 3$: $y = 5(3) - 3(3)^2 + 2 = -10$

Compare the obtained values to the tables. Therefore, the choice B is the correct answer.

10) Choice E is correct
To find the values of x when $x^2 + 2x - 8 = -5$ through the given graph, it is enough to intercept the graph with line $y = -5$. The obtained points are equivalent to the requested values. Look at the graph below:

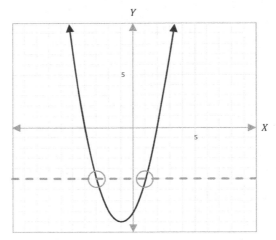

We see that line $y = -5$ intersects the graph at points $x = 1$ and $x = -3$. Therefore, choice E is correct.

11) Choice C is correct
The slope of both graphs is positive. So, to make graph g, the slope of graph f must be multiplied by a positive number. In addition, the slope of the graph g is steeper than the original graph. Therefore, the slope of the graph g is multiplied by a number greater than one. On the other hand, we can see that graph g is 4 units higher than the graph f. The only choice that meets these conditions is option C.

12) Choice D is correct
Based on the information in the table, the function g is decreasing. So, choices 1 and 2 are false. Next, by dividing each value of g by its previous value, we get:

$\frac{9,750}{10,000} = 0.975$, $\frac{9,506}{9,750} \cong 0.975$, $\cdots$, and $\frac{9,037}{9,269} \cong 0.975$.

We can see that the values of the function are changing with a ratio of 0.975 or 97.5%. In other words, the values of the function are decreasing with a ratio of 97.5% = (100 − 2.5)%. The reduction percentage is 2.5 or $2\frac{1}{2}$.

13) Choice B is correct

We know that xy is equal to yx. So, rewrite the expression as follow:

$(xy + 7z − 2xy) − (3xy − z)$

Now, combine like terms and simplify:

$(xy + 7z − 2xy) − (3xy − z) = xy + 7z − 2xy − 3xy + z$
$$= (7z + z) + (xy − 2xy − 3xy)$$
$$= 8z − 4xy$$

14) The answer is 8

$x^2 + 6x + r = (x + 2)(x + p) = x^2 + (2 + p)x + 2p$, on the left side of the equation the coefficient of x is 6, and on the right side of the equation, the coefficient of x is $2 + p$. Thus

$2 + p = 6 \rightarrow p = 4$ and $r = 2p = 2(4) = 8$.

15) Choice A is correct

If $f(x) = 3x + 4(x + 1) + 2$, then find $f(4x)$ by substituting $4x$ for every x in the function. This gives: $f(4x) = 3(4x) + 4(4x + 1) + 2$,

It simplifies to: $f(4x) = 3(4x) + 4(4x + 1) + 2 = 12x + 16x + 4 + 2 = 28x + 6$.

16) Choice B is correct

To solve the system of equations:

$3x + y = 15$
$−2x + 4y = 10$

We can use the method of elimination. We want to eliminate one of the variables, so we can start by eliminating x by multiplying the second equation by $\frac{3}{2}$ to get:

$3x + y = 15$
$\frac{3}{2} \times (−2x + 4y) = \frac{3}{2} \times (10) \rightarrow$
$3x + y = 15$
$−3x + 6y = 15$

Next, we can add the two equations to eliminate y and solve for x:

$3x + y + (−3x + 6y) = 15 + 15 \rightarrow 7y = 30 \rightarrow y = \frac{30}{7}$.

Now, substitute $y = \frac{30}{7}$, in the first equation and solve:

$$3x + \left(\frac{30}{7}\right) = 15 \rightarrow 3x = 15 - \frac{30}{7} \rightarrow 3x = \frac{105-30}{7} = \frac{75}{7}$$

$$\rightarrow x = \frac{25}{7} =$$

Therefore, the solution of a system of equations is $\left(\frac{25}{7}, \frac{30}{7}\right)$, which means the answer is option B.

17) Choice D is correct

The smallest y-coordinate belongs to the point with coordinates $(3, -4)$.

The minimum value of the graph is $f(3) = -4$. Therefore, the value of $f(x)$ is at its minimum when x equals to 3.

18) Choice E is correct

Expanding the left side of the equation and simplifying, we get:

$$1 + 3\,m - 12 = 7\,m \rightarrow 3\,m - 11 = 7\,m.$$

Subtracting $3\,m$, we get: $-11 = 4\,m$. Dividing both sides by 4, we get $x = -\frac{11}{4}$.

Therefore, the solution to the equation is choice E, $x = -\frac{11}{4} = -2.75$.

19) Choice D is correct

For this purpose, it is necessary that each ordered pair of the content question is available in the corresponding relationship. Now, Check them out:

A. For the ordered pair $(0,3)$, if $x = 0$, then $g(0) = (0)^2 + 2(0) - 3 = -3$. Therefore, It's Not true!

B. In choice B, the ordered pair is as follows: $(-3, -5)$, $(-1, -4)$, $(0,0)$, and $(2,4)$. which is different from the content of the question.

C. Choice C is similar to choice B.

D. Choice D represents the same relationship as g. All the points of the function g are marked in graph D below:

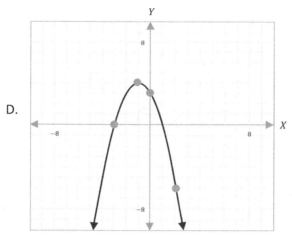

E. For the ordered pair $(-1,4)$, if $x = -1$, then $g(-1) = 2(-1)^2 + (-1) - 19 = -18$. Therefore, It's Not true!

20) The answer is 6

We must first calculate the slope of the function f. Given that function f passes through points $(-2, 1)$ and $(0, 4)$, its slope is equal to: $\frac{4-1}{0-(-2)} = \frac{3}{2}$.

The slope of the line perpendicular to this line is $m_1 \times m_2 = -1 \Rightarrow \frac{3}{2} \times m_2 = -1 \Rightarrow m_2 = -\frac{2}{3}$.

The equation that defines function g passes through the point $(0, 4)$ is:

$$g(x) = -\frac{2}{3}x + b \to 4 = -\frac{2}{3}(0) + b \to 4 = 0 + b \to b = 4.$$

So, the equation of g is $g(x) = -\frac{2}{3}x + 4$.

The point of collision of function g with the x-axis is obtained by placing 0 instead of y in the function. Then: $0 = -\frac{2}{3}x + 4 \to \frac{2}{3}x = 4 \to x = 6$.

21) Choice A is correct.

$$\frac{\frac{x+3}{x^2-9}}{\frac{x-2}{x-3}} = \frac{(x+3) \times (x-3)}{(x^2-9) \times (x-2)}, (x^2 - 9) = x^2 - 3^2 = (x - 3)(x + 3),$$

Then: $\frac{(x+3)(x-3)}{(x-3)(x+3)(x-2)} = \frac{1}{(x-2)}$

22) Choice C is correct.

Line C is the graph of $x = -3$.

23) Choice E is correct.

Apply absolute equation rule $-3 \leq 9 + 6x \leq 3$. Add -9 to all sides. Then:

$-3 - 9 \leq 9 + 6x - 9 \leq 3 - 9 \rightarrow -12 \leq 6x \leq -6$. Now, divide all sides by 6:

$-2 \leq x \leq -1$. Choice E represents this inequality.

24) Choice D is correct.

To solve $\frac{a}{4} + \frac{1}{2} = \frac{3}{a-2}$, first multiply by the least common multiplier $4(a - 2)$. Then:

$\frac{a}{4} \cdot 4(a - 2) + \frac{1}{2} \cdot 4(a - 2) = \frac{3}{a-2} \cdot 4(a - 2)$. Now, simplify: $a(a - 2) + 2(a - 2) = 12 \rightarrow$

$a^2 - 2a + 2a - 4 = 12 \rightarrow a^2 = 16 \rightarrow a = \sqrt{16} \rightarrow a = -4, a = 4$

25) Choice A is correct.

The graph of $y = f(x)$ crosses the x-axis at $x = -3$ and $x = 1$, and crosses the y-axis at $y = -3$, and has its vertex at the point $(-1, -4)$. Therefore, the ordered pairs $(-3, 0)$, $(1, 0)$, $(0, -3)$, and $(-1, -4)$ must satisfy the equation for $f(x)$. Furthermore, because the graph opens up-ward, the equation defining $f(x)$ must have positive leading coefficient. All of these conditions are met by the equation: $f(x) = x^2 + 2x - 3$

26) Choice D is correct.

First, find the equation of the line. Two points on the line are $(0, -2)$ and $(2, 0)$. The slope of the line is 1 and the equation of the line is: $y = x - 2$. Only Choices D is similar to the equation of the line.

27) Choice E is correct.

A. $x^{-2} = \frac{1}{x^2}$ This is true.

B. $(x^2)^3 = x^6$ This is true.

C. $x^6 - 5x^2 = x^2(x^3 - 5)$ This is true.

D. $\left(3 - \frac{a}{6}\right)\left(3 + \frac{a}{6}\right) = 9 - \frac{a^2}{36}$ This is true.

E. $4x^2 - 16x + 8 = (2x - 4)^2$ This is incorrect: $4x^2 - 16x + 16 = (2x - 4)^2$

28) Choice B is correct.

Take the number outside the parenthesis and distribute it to the numbers inside.

$$\sqrt{3}(\sqrt{3} - 4) = \sqrt{3}.\sqrt{3} - \sqrt{3}.4$$

When multiplying a number inside and a number outside the radical symbol, simply place them side by side: $\sqrt{3}.\sqrt{3} - \sqrt{3}.4 = \sqrt{9} - 4\sqrt{3} = 3 - 4\sqrt{3}$

29) Choice D is correct.

We know that $\left(\frac{g}{h}\right)(x) = \frac{g(x)}{h(x)}$. Since $g(x) = 3x^2 + 24x$ and $h(x) = x + 8$, we can find $\frac{g(x)}{h(x)}$ by simplifying $g(x)$: $\frac{g(x)}{h(x)} = \frac{3x^2+24x}{x+8} = \frac{3x(x+8)}{x+8} = 3x$

30) Choice D is correct.

The perimeter of the shape is the sum of all its sides:

Perimeter $= 5x + 3x + (x + y) + 2y$. Now, combine like terms:
$5x + 3x + (x + y) + 2y = 9x + 3y$

31) Choice B is correct.

First divide the numerator $(12x^2 + 8x^3 + 24)$ by 4: $\frac{12x^2+8x^3+24}{4} = 3x^2 + 2x^3 + 6$

Arranging the exponents in the descending order, we get the standard form of the polynomial: $2x^3 + 3x^2 + 6$

32) Choice C is correct.

Use the definition of a negative exponent. $x^{-n} = \frac{1}{x^n} \rightarrow (-5)^{-3} = \frac{1}{(-5)^3} = -\frac{1}{125}$

33) Choice B is correct.

Quotient rule: $log\frac{x}{y} = log\,x - log\,y$, Product rule: $log(xy) = log\,x + log\,y$,

Power rule: $log\,x^n = n\,log\,x$. Using the above rules, we can expand the logarithm.

$$log\frac{a^2b^2}{c^4} = (log\,a^2b^2) - (log\,c^2) = log\,a^2 + log\,b^2 - log\,c^4 = 2\,log\,a + 2\,log\,b - 4\,log\,c$$

34) Choice E is correct.

When finding the domain of a fractional function, you must exclude all the x values that make the denominator equal to zero, because you can never divide by zero.

$$x^2 - 9 = 0 \rightarrow (x + 3)(x - 3) = 0 \rightarrow x = 3, -3$$

Domain = all real numbers except 3 and -3.

35) Choice E is correct.

The highest exponent will be the degree of the polynomial.

In expression $-8x^2 + 5x^4 + 9 - 3x^3$, the highest exponent is 4. Then, its degree is 4. So, choice E is correct.

36) Choice D is correct.

The vertex form of a parabola is $y = a(x - h)^2 + k$ where (h, k) is the vertex. So, $(-9, -5)$ is the vertex of parabola $y = (x + 9)^2 - 5$.

37) Choice E is correct.

One side of square $= a$

Area of square $= a \times a \rightarrow (1 + \sqrt{6})(1 + \sqrt{6}) = 1 + \sqrt{6} + \sqrt{6} + 6 = 7 + 2\sqrt{6}$

38) Choice D is correct.

You can use a general formula to find the formula for the sequence. The formula is: $a_n = a_1 + d(n - 1)$.

From the first two term and the difference between the first term and the second term is $9 - 5 = 4$. Just plug these numbers into formula and the simplify:

$a_n = 5 + 4(n - 1) \rightarrow a_n = 5 + 4n - 4 \rightarrow a_n = 4n + 1$

39) Choice A is correct.

First replace $g(x)$ with y. Then: $y = 5x - 7$

Next, replace all $x's$ with y and all $y's$ with x. $x = 5y - 7$

Now, solve for y. $5y = x + 7 \rightarrow y = \frac{x+7}{5}$

Finally replace y with $g^{-1}(x)$: $g^{-1}(x) = \frac{x+7}{5}$

40) Choice C is correct.

The standard form of a quadratic equation looks like this: $ax^2 + bx + c = 0$

Where a, b, and c are the numerical coefficients of the terms of the quadratic, the value of the variable x is given by the following equation: $x = \frac{-b \pm \sqrt{b^2 - 4ac}}{2a}$.

$x^2 + 7x + 6 = 0$. In this equation, $a = 1, b = 7, c = 6$

Now, we can use the quadratic formula: $x = \frac{-b \pm \sqrt{b^2 - 4ac}}{2a}$

Just plug in the values of a, b, and c, and do the calculations. $x_{1,2} = \frac{-7 \pm \sqrt{7^2 - 4(1)(6)}}{2(1)} = \frac{-7 \pm 5}{2} = -6, -1$

College Algebra Practice Test 2

Answers and Explanations

1) Choice A is correct

If $x - a$ is a factor of $g(x)$, then $g(a)$ must equal 0. Based on the table $g(-1) = 0$ and $g(5) = 0$. Therefore, $x + 1$ and $x - 5$ are factors of $g(x)$.

2) Choice B is correct

A column of 29 stacked wooden sheets is about $60\frac{3}{5}$ centimeters tall, which is slightly less than 61 centimeters tall. Therefore, a column of stacked wooden sheets that is 61 centimeters tall would contain slightly more than 29 wooden sheets. It can then be reasoned that because 122 meters are twice 61 meters, a column of stacked wooden sheets that is 122 meters tall would contain slightly more than twice as many wooden sheets; that is, slightly more than 58 wooden sheets. An alternate approach is to write proportion that compares the column height to the number of wooden sheets, or $\frac{60\frac{3}{5}\ meters}{29\ wooden\ sheets} = \frac{122\ meters}{x\ wooden\ sheets}$, where x is the number of coins in a 122-centimeter-tall column. Multiplying each side of the proportion gives $60\frac{3}{5}x = 3,538 \rightarrow \frac{303}{5}x = 3,538$. Solving for x gives $x = \frac{3,538 \times 5}{303}$, which is approximately 58. Therefore, of the given choices, 59 is closest to the number of wooden sheets it would take to build a 122-centimeter-tall column.

3) Choice E is correct

Subtracting 29 from both sides of the equation $a = 2.35b + 29$ gives $a - 29 = 2.35b$. Then dividing both sides of $a - 29 = 2.35b$ by 2.35 gives $b = \frac{a-29}{2.35}$.

4) Choice B is correct

Rearrange the ordered pair from the smallest value of the first component to the biggest value.

$\{(-2,7), (-1,2), (0, -1), (3,2), (5,14)\}$

Since the range of the function is first decreasing and then increasing with the increase of x, we conclude that between the choices, only the parent function of quadratic has this property.

5) Choice B is correct

Since the basketball player scored at least 15 points more than the previous record, we can write $p \geq r + 15$.

This inequality ensures that p is at least 15 more than r, and thus all possible values of p in terms of r are given by this inequality. Therefore, the answer is B.

6) Choice E is correct

The total length of the suspension bridge, including the towers, can be found by adding the length of the n bridge sections to the height of the two towers. Each section is $48.2m$ long and there are n sections, so the length of the bridge sections is $48.2n$. The height of the two towers is $125.6m$ each, so their total height is $2 \times 125.6 = 251.2m$. Therefore, the function that can be used to find the total length of the bridge in meters, including the towers, is:

$$L(x) = 48.2n + 251.2$$

So, the correct answer is E.

7) Choice A is correct

Since the cost of shipping a package varies directly with its weight, we can use the formula $y = kx$, where y is the cost, x is the weight, and k is the constant of proportionality.

We are given that the cost of shipping a 4-pound package is $10.80, so we can set up an equation using this information: $10.80 = k(4)$. Solving for k, we get $k = 2.7$.

Now, we can use this value of k to find the cost of shipping a 2.5-pound package:

$$y = 2.7(2.5) = 6.75.$$

Therefore, the cost of shipping a 2.5-pound package is $6.75, which is answer A.

8) Choice D is correct

To find the $x-$intercepts of the graph of the quadratic function, we need to set $g(x) = 0$ and solve for x. For the function $g(x) = -3x^2 + 9x - 6$, we have: $-3x^2 + 9x - 6 = 0$. Dividing both sides by -3, we get $x^2 - 3x + 2 = 0$.

To solve this quadratic equation, we can use the quadratic formula:

$$x_{1,2} = \frac{-b \pm \sqrt{b^2 - 4ac}}{2a}$$

where $a = 1$, $b = -3$, and $c = 2$.

Plugging in these values, we get:

$$x_{1,2} = \frac{-(-3) \pm \sqrt{(-3)^2 - 4(1)(2)}}{2(1)} = \frac{3 \pm \sqrt{9 - 8}}{2} = \frac{3 \pm 1}{2}$$

So, the $x-$intercepts of the graph of the function $g(x)$ are $x = 2$ and $x = 1$.

9) Choice D is correct

Since 8 can be rewritten as 2^3, $8^{\frac{2}{5}}$ is equivalent to $2^{3\left(\frac{2}{5}\right)}$. Applying the properties of exponents gives $2^{3 \times \frac{2}{5}} = 2^{\frac{6}{5}}$. This can be written as $2^{\frac{5}{5}} \cdot 2^{\frac{1}{5}}$, $2^{\frac{5}{5}}$ is equal to 2, and $2^{\frac{1}{5}}$ is equal to $\sqrt[5]{2}$ (remember $b^{\frac{m}{n}} = \sqrt[n]{b^m}$). So, $8^{\frac{2}{5}}$ is equal to $2\sqrt[5]{2}$.

10) Choice C is correct

Since the graph crosses the y-axis at $(0, r)$, then substituting 0 for x and r for y in $r = -3(0)^2 + 12(0) + 6$ creates a true statement: $r = -3(0)^2 + 12(0) + 6$, or $r = 6$.

Choice C represents the chart.

11) Choice C is correct

Let a equal the number of 120-pound packages, and let b equal the number of 100-pound packages. It's given that the total weight of the packages can be at most 1,100 pounds: the inequality $120a + 100b \leq 1,100$ represents this situation. It's also given that the helicopter must carry at least 10 packages: the inequality $a + b \geq 10$ represents this situation. Values of a and b that satisfy these two inequalities represent the allowable numbers of 120-pound packages and 100-pound packages the helicopter can transport. To maximize the number of 120-pound packages, a, in the helicopter, the number of 100-pound packages, b, in the helicopter needs to be minimized. Expressing b in terms of a in the second inequality yields $b \geq 10 - a$, so the minimum value of b is equal to $10 - a$. Substituting $10 - a$ for b in the first inequality results in

$120a + 100(10 - a) \leq 1,100$. Using the distributive property to rewrite this inequality yields $120a + 1,000 - 100a \leq 1,100$ or $20a + 1,000 \leq 1,100$. Subtracting $1,000$ from both sides of this inequality yields $20a \leq 100$. Dividing both sides of this inequality by 20 results in $a \leq 5$. This means that the maximum number of 120-pound packages that the helicopter can carry per trip is 5.

12) Choice E is correct

The equation of a line with slope m and passing through the point (x_1, y_1) can be written as $y - y_1 = m(x - x_1)$. In this case, we are given that the slope is 2 and the point $(3,5)$ is on the line. So, we have $y - 5 = 2(x - 3)$. Expanding the right-hand side gives $y - 5 = 2x - 6$. Adding 5 to both sides gives $y = 2x - 1$.

Therefore, the equation of the line is A.

13) Choice D is correct

The solution of the equation $y = 3$ is equivalent to the intersection of the graph $y = mx + b$ and the horizontal line $y = 3$. Look at the graph below.

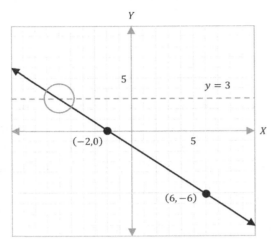

The intersection is the ordered pair $(-6,3)$. The first component of this ordered pair is -6 and is equivalent to the solution of the problem. Choice D is the correct answer.

In another way, you can get the correct answer by writing the equation of the graph $y = mx + b$. Next, solve the equation $mx + b = 3$.

14) The answer is 2

The line k is parallel to the line $y = \frac{3}{4}x + 3$ so they have the same slopes. The slope of the line $y = \frac{3}{4}x + 3$ line is $\frac{3}{4}$. Therefore, the slope of the line k is also equal to $\frac{3}{4}$.

So, the equation of line k in the slope-intercept form is $y = \frac{3}{4}x - 7$.

By placing the point m on the line k, the value of b will be equal to:

$b = \frac{3}{4}(12) - 7 \rightarrow b = 9 - 7 \rightarrow b = 2.$

15) Choice A is correct

According to the table, the value of y increases by $\frac{21}{10} - \frac{8}{5} = \frac{21-16}{10} = \frac{5}{10} = \frac{1}{2}$ every time the value of x increases by 1. It follows that the simplest equation relating y to x is linear and of the form $y = \frac{1}{2}x + b$ for some constant b. Furthermore, the ordered pair $\left(2, \frac{8}{5}\right)$ from the table must satisfy this equation. Substituting 2 for x and $\frac{8}{5}$ for y in the equation $y = \frac{1}{2}x + b$ gives $\frac{8}{5} = \frac{1}{2}(2) + b$. Solving this equation for b gives $b = \frac{3}{5}$. Therefore, the equation in choice A correctly relates y to x.

16) Choice B is correct

To solve this problem, let e represent the number of evening dresses, and c represent the number of cocktail dresses. We can set up a system of two equations based on the given information:

$e + c = 200$ (The total number of dresses)

$\frac{e}{c} = \frac{3}{5} \rightarrow e = \frac{3}{5}c$ (There are $\frac{3}{5}$ times as many evening dresses as cocktail dresses)

Substitute the second equation into the first equation to get: $\frac{3}{5}c + c = 200$. Simplify and solve for c: $\frac{8}{5}c = 200 \rightarrow c = 125$. Use the second equation to find e: $e = \frac{3}{5} \times 125 = 75$.

Therefore, there are 75 evening dresses and 125 cocktail dresses on display. The answer is B.

17) Choice B is correct

To find the greatest value in the range for renting a bicycle from the rental shop, we need to consider the different scenarios that can occur based on the number of hours rented:

- If the bicycle is rented for 5 or fewer hours, the cost will be $10 per hour.
- If the bicycle is rented for more than 5 hours, the cost will be $65 ($50 for the first 5 hours and $15 for the late fee).

Therefore, the greatest value in the range for this situation is $65, which is the maximum cost that can be charged regardless of how many hours the bicycle is rented beyond the first 5 hours.

18) Choice A is correct

To find the average annual electricity consumption of the town, we need to multiply the average monthly consumption by 12:

$$500\,\frac{kWh}{month} \times 12\,\frac{month}{year} = 6,000\,\frac{kWh}{year}$$

For the first six months, the town consumed $2,800 kWh$. So, the town needs to consume:

$$6,000 kWh - 2,800 kWh = 3,200 kWh$$

For the rest of the year.

If the town is expected to consume between 400 and $550 kWh$ per month for the rest of the year, it will take at least 6 months to consume $3,200 kWh$. Therefore, the answer is A.

19) Choice D is correct

To solve the problem, first multiply $5a$ by $\left(\frac{1}{5}a - 2\right)$ and -2 by $\left(4 - \frac{5}{2}a\right)$. We get:

$$5a\left(\frac{1}{5}a - 2\right) = 5a \times \frac{1}{5}a - 5a \times 2 = a^2 - 10a$$

$$-2\left(4 - \tfrac{5}{2}a\right) = (-2) \times 4 - (-2) \times \tfrac{5}{2}a = -8 + 5a$$

Next, add the obtained expressions together: $a^2 - 10a - 8 + 5a$. Now, combine like terms. Therefore:

$$5a\left(\tfrac{1}{5}a - 2\right) - 2\left(4 - \tfrac{5}{2}a\right) = a^2 - 5a - 8$$

20) The answer is 80

Let x be the number of kilometers that is equal to 50 miles. Since 10 miles is equal to 16 kilometers, it follows that $\frac{50}{10} = \frac{x}{16}$. Solving this proportion for x yields $10x = 800$ or $x = 80$.

21) Choice C is correct.

To solve for x, isolate the radical on one side of the equation. Divide both sides by 4. Then: $4\sqrt{2x+9} = 28 \rightarrow \frac{4\sqrt{2x+9}}{4} = \frac{28}{4} \rightarrow \sqrt{2x+9} = 7$. Square both sides:

$\left(\sqrt{(2x+9)}\right)^2 = 7^2$. Then: $2x + 9 = 49 \rightarrow 2x = 40 \rightarrow x = 20$. Substitute x by 20 in the original equation and check the answer: $x = 20 \rightarrow 4\sqrt{2(20)+9} = 4\sqrt{49} = 4(7) = 28$

22) Choice D is correct.

Based on the table provided: $g(-2) = g(x = -2) = 3 \rightarrow g(3) = g(x = 3) = -2$

$$3g(-2) - 2g(3) = 3(3) - 2(-2) = 9 + 4 = 13$$

23) Choice C is correct.

The general form of absolute function is: $f(x) = a|x - h| + k$

Since the graph opens downward with a slope of 1, then a is negative one. The graph moved 1 unit up, so the value of k is 1. Then, choice C is correct. $y = -|x| + 1$

24) Choice A is correct.

$\sqrt{x} = 4 \rightarrow x = 16$, then; $\sqrt{x} - 7 = \sqrt{16} - 7 = 4 - 7 = -3$ and $\sqrt{x - 7} = \sqrt{16 - 7} = \sqrt{9} = 3$

Then: $\left(\sqrt{x-7}\right) + \left(\sqrt{x} - 7\right) = 3 + (-3) = 0$

25) Choice D is correct.

$\sin A = \frac{1}{3} \Rightarrow$ Since $\sin \theta = \frac{opposite}{hypotenuse}$, we have the following right triangle.

Then: $c = \sqrt{3^2 - 1^2} = \sqrt{9 - 1} = \sqrt{8}$. Then: $\cos A = \frac{opposite}{Adjacent} = \frac{\sqrt{8}}{3}$

26) Choice E is correct.

Plug in the value of each choice in the inequality.

A. 1 $(1-2)^2 + 1 > 3(1) - 1 \rightarrow 2 > 2$ This is Not true.

B. 3 $(3-2)^2 + 1 > 3(3) - 1 \rightarrow 2 > 8$ This is Not true.

C. 4 $(4-2)^2 + 1 > 3(4) - 1 \rightarrow 5 > 11$ This is Not true.

D. 6 $(6-2)^2 + 1 > 3(6) - 1 \rightarrow 17 > 17$ This is Not true.

E. 8 $(8-2)^2 + 1 > 3(8) - 1 \rightarrow 37 > 23$ This is true.

27) Choice C is correct.

To solve for the variable, isolate it on one side of the equation. For this equation, multiply both sides by 5. Then: $\frac{3x}{5} = 27 \rightarrow \frac{3x}{5} \times 5 = 27 \times 5 \rightarrow 3x = 135$

Now, divide both sides by 3: $x = \frac{135}{3} = 45$

28) Choice E is correct.

$81 = 3^{2x}$. Convert to base 3: $81 = 3^{2x} = 3^4 = 3^{2x}$. If $a^{f(x)} = b^{g(x)}$, then $f(x) = g(x)$

Therefore: $4 = 2x \rightarrow x = \frac{4}{2} \rightarrow x = 2$

29) Choice B is correct.

Use FOIL (First-Out-In-Last) method: $-(2-i)(i-2) = -2i + 4 + i^2 - 2i = -4i + i^2 + 4$. Combine like terms: $(2i - 3) - 4i + i^2 + 4 = -2i + i^2 + 1 = -2i + (-1) + 1 = -2i$

30) Choice D is correct.

In the function $f(x) = \frac{4x^2 - 6x + 12}{9 - x}$, the denominator cannot be zero. Then, $9 - x \neq 0 \rightarrow x \neq 9$. So, $f(9)$ is not defined.

31) Choice D is correct.

Multiplying each side of $-3x - y = 6$ by 2 gives $-6x - 2y = 12$. Adding each side of $-6x - 2y = 12$ to the corresponding side of $6x + 4y = 10$ gives $2y = 22$, or $y = 11$. Finally, substituting 11 for y in $6x + 4y = 10$ gives $6x + 4(11) = 10$, or $x = -\frac{17}{3}$.

32) Choice C is correct.

Find a common denominator and simplify: $\frac{3x-2}{x-3} - \frac{x-4}{3x-2} = \frac{(3x-2)^2 - (x-4)(x-3)}{(x-3)(3x-2)} =$

$\frac{(3x)^2 - 2(3x)(2) - 2^2 + (-x+4)(x-3)}{(x-3)(3x-2)} = \frac{9x^2 - 12x + 4 - x^2 + 3x + 4x - 12}{(x-3)(3x-2)} = \frac{8x^2 - 5x - 8}{(x-3)(3x-2)}$

33) Choice D is correct.

The problem asks for the sum of the roots of the quadratic equation $2n^2 + 16n + 24 = 0$. Dividing each side of the equation by 2 gives $n^2 + 8n + 12 = 0$. If the roots of

$n^2 + 8n + 12 = 0$ are n_1 and n_2, then the equation can be factored as

$n^2 + 8n + 12 = (n - n_1)(n - n_2) = 0$. Looking at the coefficient of n on each side of

$n^2 + 8n + 12 = (n + 6)(n + 2)$ gives $n = -6$ or $n = -2$, then, $-6 + (-2) = -8$

34) Choice D is correct.

To perform the division $\frac{3+2i}{5+i}$, multiply the numerator and denominator of $\frac{3+2i}{5+1i}$ by the

conjugate of the denominator, $5 - i$. This gives $\frac{(3+2i)(5-i)}{(5+1i)(5-i)} = \frac{15-3i+10i-2i^2}{5^2-i^2}$. Since $i^2 = -1$,

this can be simplified to $\frac{15-3i+10i+2}{25+1} = \frac{17+7i}{26}$.

35) Choice E is correct.

The real part of the complex number is 2, and the imaginary part is $-4i$. We plot the ordered pair $(2, -4)$, in whichthat the real number (2) is plotted on the x −axis and the imaginary part $(-4i)$ is plotted on the y −axis. Point E represents the complex number $2 - 4i$.

36) Choice A is correct.

Solve for x: $2x - 5y = 10 \rightarrow x - \frac{5}{2}y = 5 \rightarrow x = \frac{5}{2}y + 5$

37) Choice B is correct.

Simplify the numerator: $\frac{x+(5x)^2+(3x)^3}{x} = \frac{x+5^2x^2+3^3x^3}{x} = \frac{x+25x^2+27x^3}{x}$

Pull an x out of each term in the numerator. $\frac{x(1+25x+27x^2)}{x}$

The x in the numerator and the x in the denominator cancel:

$1 + 25x + 27x^2 = 27x^2 + 25x + 1$

38) Choice B is correct.

The possible y values are between -4 and 3. Range: $-4 \leq y \leq 3$

39) Choice B is correct.

$tan x = \frac{opposite}{adjacent}$, and $\tan x = \frac{8}{15}$, therefore, the opposite side of the angle x is 8 and the adjacent side is 15. Let's draw the triangle.

Using the Pythagorean theorem, we have:

$a^2 + b^2 = c^2 \rightarrow 8^2 + 15^2 = c^2 \rightarrow 64 + 225 = c^2 \rightarrow c = 17$

$sin x = \frac{opposite}{hypotenuse} = \frac{8}{17}$

40) Choice D is correct.

The vertex form of a parabola is $y = a(x - h)^2 + k$, where (h, k) is the vertex. The variable a has the same value and function as the variable in the standard form. If $a > 0$, the parabola opens up, and if $a < 0$, the parabola opens down. $-6 < 0 \rightarrow$ the parabola opens down.

Effortless Math's College Algebra Online Center

... So Much More Online!

Effortless Math Online College Algebra Center offers a complete study program, including the following:

✓ Numerous College Algebra worksheets to help you measure your math skills

✓ Complete list of College Algebra formulas

✓ Video lessons for College Algebra topics

✓ Full-length College Algebra practice tests

✓ And much more...

No Registration Required.

Visit Effortlessmath.com/CollegeALGEBRA to find your online College Algebra resources.

Receive the PDF version of this book or get another FREE book!

Thank you for using our Book!

Do you LOVE this book?

Then, you can get the PDF version of this book or another book absolutely FREE!

Please email us at:

info@EffortlessMath.com

for details.

Author's Final Note

I hope you enjoyed reading this book. You've made it through the book! Great job!

First of all, thank you for purchasing this study guide. I know you could have picked any number of books to help you prepare for your College Algebra course, but you picked this book and for that I am extremely grateful.

It took me years to write this study guide for the College Algebra because I wanted to prepare a comprehensive College Algebra study guide to help students make the most effective use of their valuable time while preparing for the final test.

After teaching and tutoring math courses for over a decade, I've gathered my personal notes and lessons to develop this study guide. It is my greatest hope that the lessons in this book could help you prepare for your test successfully.

If you have any questions, please contact me at reza@effortlessmath.com and I will be glad to assist. Your feedback will help me to greatly improve the quality of my books in the future and make this book even better. Furthermore, I expect that I have made a few minor errors somewhere in this study guide. If you think this to be the case, please let me know so I can fix the issue as soon as possible.

If you enjoyed this book and found some benefit in reading this, I'd like to hear from you and hope that you could take a quick minute to post a review on the book's Amazon page.

I personally go over every single review, to make sure my books really are reaching out and helping students and test takers. Please help me help College Algebra students, by leaving a review!

I wish you all the best in your future success!

Reza Nazari

Math teacher and author

Made in the USA
Las Vegas, NV
10 April 2024